Enid Blyton's™

ENCHANTED LANDS

The Land of Take-What-You-Want

Scholastic Children's Books,
Commonwealth House, 1-19 New Oxford Street,
London WC1A 1NU, UK
a division of Scholastic Ltd

London ~ New York ~ Toronto ~ Sydney ~ Auckland

First published in 1998 by Hippo, an imprint of Scholastic Ltd

Story consultant: Gillian Baverstock

1 2 3 4 5 6 7 8 9 10

ISBN 0 590 11179 5

Printed in Belgium by Proost

Beth, Joe and Fran followed Barney Owl through the Enchanted Wood. They were going to the Faraway Tree to visit the new land that had arrived at the top!

Beth gave a little skip of excitement when she heard the leaves rustling on the trees: "Wisha-Wisha! Wisha-Wisha!" It really was a magical sound.

As they came to the centre of the wood where the Faraway Tree grew tall, they saw their friend Silky waiting for them and heard Dame Washalot singing her scrubbing song.

"La la la la la . . .
Oooooh we scrub out the dirt
And we scrub in the whites,
Scrubbing all day long
And far into the night . . ."

Dame Washalot lived half-way up the Faraway Tree. The door to her little room in the tree was open, and steam and soapsuds drifted out of it.

She had just finished a batch of washing. She lifted the huge, zinc tub full of dirty water and emptied it down the tree just as Joe, Beth and Fran were starting to climb it.

"Watch out!" warned Silky, pointing upwards.

Joe looked up the tree as Dame Washalot's dirty washing water cascaded down and soaked him. He staggered backwards and ended up sitting on the ledge of a small open window.

Then something prodded Joe in the back. He jumped up and turned to see an angry face glaring through the window.

"Just what do you think you're doing, eh? Blocking all my sunshine out like that. I've a good mind to . . ."

Silky flew over and spoke to the angry little fellow. Then, mumbling to himself, the little man went back into his house.

"Who was that?" Beth asked Silky.

"Don't mind him. We call him Mr Watzisname because he can never remember his name," said Silky. "Now come on," she added, "or we'll be late!"

They climbed up
and up and up the tree
until they came to the
topmost branch where
their friends, Moonface
and Saucepan Man,
were waiting for them.

"What's the land at the top of the tree today, Moonface?" Beth asked.

"It's the Land of Take-What-You-Want!" he replied.

"Honestly!" said Saucepan Man, looking at Moonface. "You'd forget your own head if it wasn't so big. It's the Land of Take-What-You-Want up there!"

"That's what I said!" Moonface shouted.

"Going to bed? But it's only half past eleven!" said Saucepan Man, puzzled.

Fran laughed and shook her head. The clanging of Saucepan Man's pots and kettles and pans had made him rather deaf. He was always mishearing what people said to him.

Moonface started to climb the ladder. The others followed him. They climbed up the ladder and through the clouds that swirled around the entrance to the Land of Take-What-You-Want.

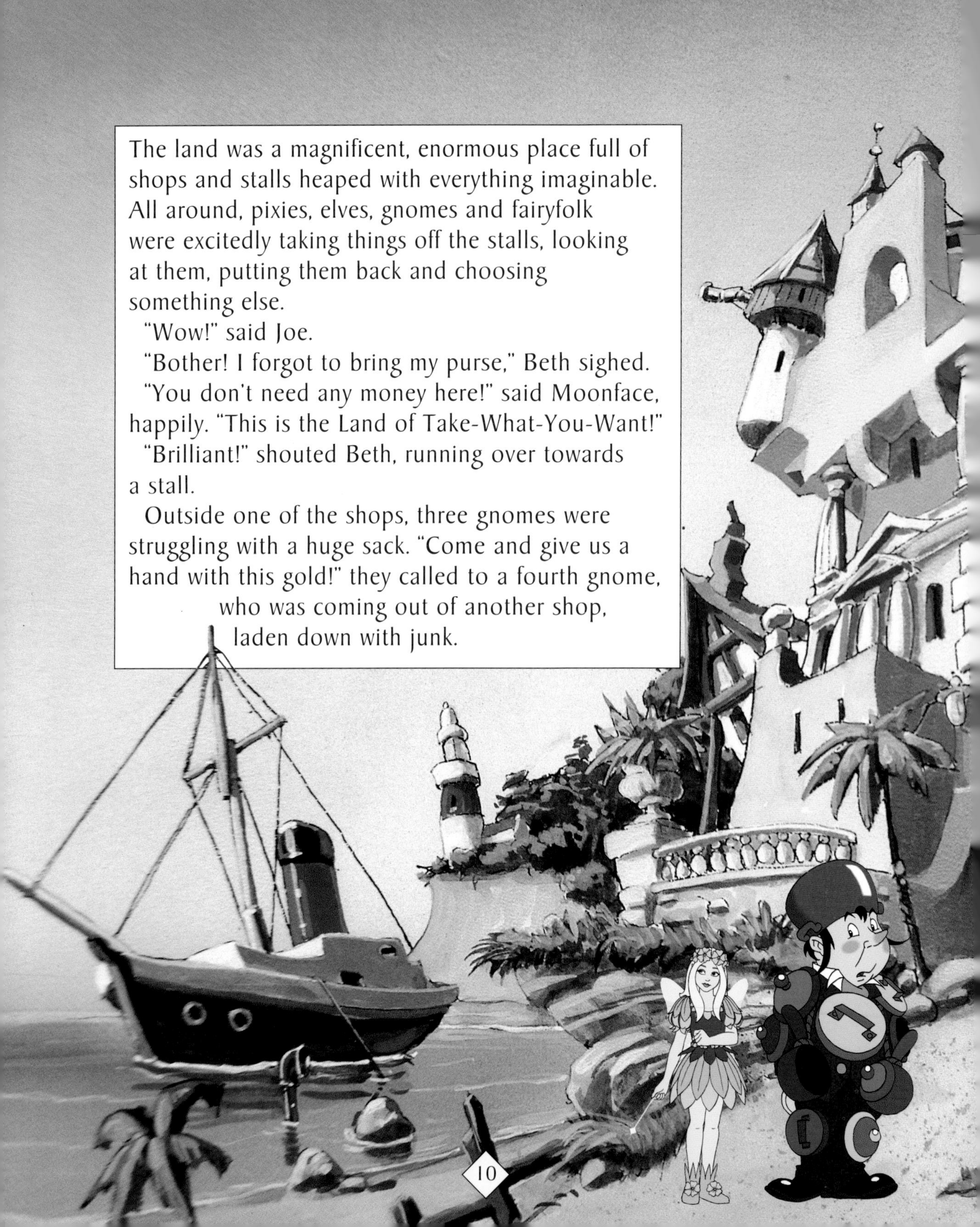

The land was a magnificent, enormous place full of shops and stalls heaped with everything imaginable. All around, pixies, elves, gnomes and fairyfolk were excitedly taking things off the stalls, looking at them, putting them back and choosing something else.

"Wow!" said Joe.

"Bother! I forgot to bring my purse," Beth sighed.

"You don't need any money here!" said Moonface, happily. "This is the Land of Take-What-You-Want!"

"Brilliant!" shouted Beth, running over towards a stall.

Outside one of the shops, three gnomes were struggling with a huge sack. "Come and give us a hand with this gold!" they called to a fourth gnome, who was coming out of another shop, laden down with junk.

Fran had wandered off but Joe and Beth looked at each other in excitement.

Joe gasped. "Gold? Did they say . . . ?"

"Yes!" said Beth. "And it's all free!" She jumped as she felt something sniffing at her ear. She swung round and found herself looking at an elephant. A big, friendly smiley elephant!

"He's mine," said Fran. "I'm going to call him Rupert. I'll take him home and he can live in the garden shed."

Fran had all sorts of other ideas for Rupert but Joe told her she'd never get an elephant back down the Faraway Tree!

Fran realised her brother was right, so she said a sad 'goodbye' to Rupert. The elephant patted her on the head with his trunk and lumbered off.

Suddenly, they saw Saucepan Man coming down from the sky! He landed in front of them with a jangling-jingling, crashing-clashing noise.

"Whee-heee!" shrieked Saucepan Man and he bounced back up!

"He's flying!" said Joe. "Look at him go!"

Just then Moonface arrived and showed them a bit of string.

"I'm sure it's very nice string," said Beth. "But . . . "

"Ha ha! Just ... "

But Moonface was interrupted by Saucepan Man who came down from the sky again.

"Pretty good, huh?" he said.

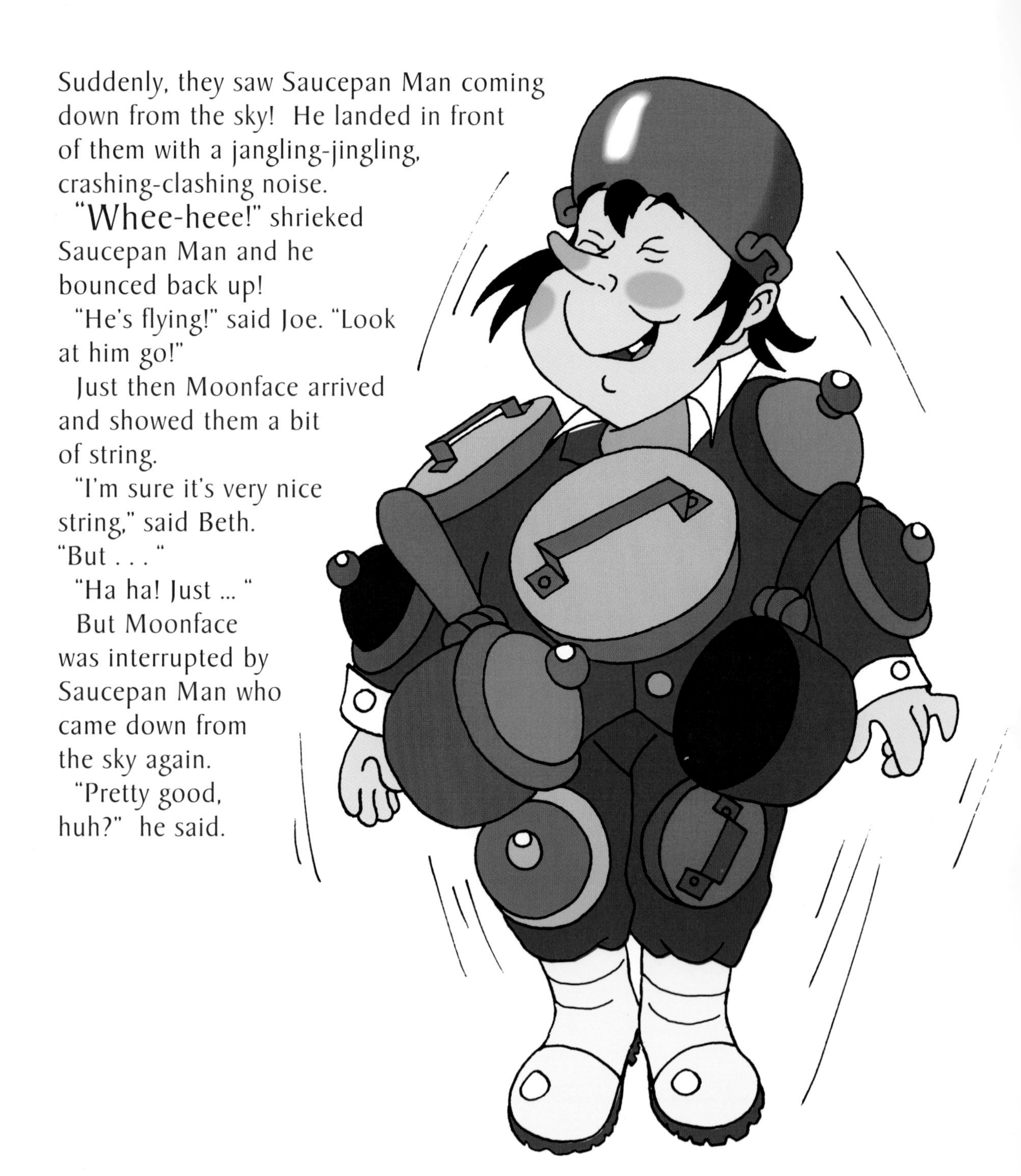

"You're wearing anti-gravity boots!" exclaimed Moonface.

"Not roots – boots!" said Saucepan. "Watch!"

And he leapt skywards again with a loud

"Whaaaa-hoooo!"

Fran was longing to know about Moonface's string.

"What's it for, Moonface?" she asked.

Moonface smiled and pulled at the dangling end of the string. There was a bright flash of red and a small kite appeared. Before Fran could blink, it became bigger and bigger and the string seemed to stretch and s-t-r-e-t-c-h—

Moonface was standing on tiptoe now. He managed to grab Fran's hand.
"Come on!" he cried. And they were both whisked away to join Saucepan Man performing aerobatics in the sky.
Joe and Beth watched for a few minutes, then Silky arrived with a walking, talking musical clock.
"Isn't Tock wonderful?" said Silky, as the clock played a tune on his bells and sang a song. "I've always wanted a talking clock!"
"Now you've got one," said Tock. "At the third stroke, the time will be twelve twenty-seven and thirty seconds . . ." And sounding just like a pig, Tock grunted three times.

Moonface, Fran and the kite were still cleverly sky-dancing with Saucepan Man. They looked as if they were really enjoying themselves! Beth decided it was about time she and Joe found something exciting, too.

They ran off, leaving Silky and Tock jigging to the sound of Tock's musical bells.

"Did you find anything, Beth?" asked Joe as they came out of an arcade.

Beth pointed to the necklace she was wearing. It was a magic necklace. Every time Beth closed her eyes and wished, swirling lights danced around and her clothes changed into new and exciting outfits.

Joe felt a little jealous. He hadn't found anything special yet. He went back to the stalls and looked at all sorts of things.

"What I really want," Joe sighed, "is . . . "

Moonface dashed up. "Joe! Joe, come quickly!" he shouted. "We forgot the time and the land's on the move!"

Moonface took Joe by the arm and hurried him away from the market to where Beth, Fran, Saucepan Man, Silky and Tock were waiting.

They all ran towards the hole in the clouds where the ladder should be.

But the ladder wasn't there. They were stranded!

"What are we going to do?" asked Beth, in a worried voice.

"Don't you like it here?" Tock asked.

Beth nodded. "I did . . . but . . . well, now I want to go home. It's all very well being able to take-what-you-want, but if you haven't got anywhere to take it . . ."

"I didn't even get to find what I wanted!" Joe said.

"What did you want?" asked Tock.

Joe just sighed.

Tock began to make whirring, tinkling noises. "You wanted an aeroplane!" he told Joe. "Come along. I know just the very thing for you," he added, dragging Joe to his feet.

Joe thought he might as well take a look. After all, he had all the time in the world now!

And a few minutes later, Tock was hauling open two large doors in an outbuilding by the market hall.

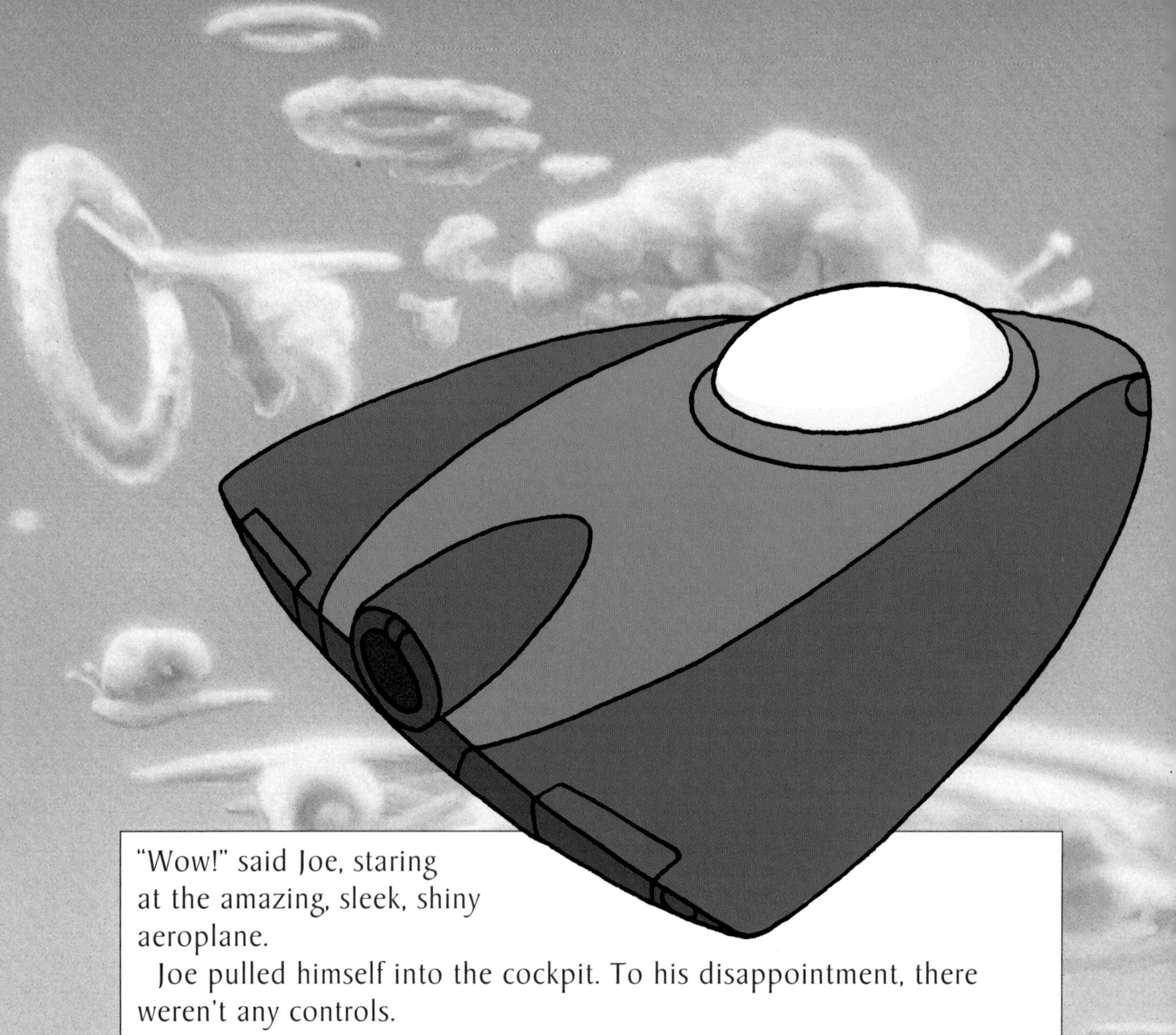

"Wow!" said Joe, staring at the amazing, sleek, shiny aeroplane.

Joe pulled himself into the cockpit. To his disappointment, there weren't any controls.

"There's a helmet in the cockpit. Put it on!" called Tock. "The plane runs on thought power. So think it into the air and fly!"

While Joe was thinking, the others were sitting miserably by the hole in the clouds where the ladder should have been.

"What's that noise?" asked Fran, suddenly.

"Look! It's an aeroplane coming in to land," shouted Beth. "And Joe's flying it!"

"Tock's with him too," said Silky, running over to the plane.

"All aboard!" cried Joe. "We're going home!"

They laughed and whooped as the plane swooped them down through the leaves of the Faraway Tree.

The Angry Pixie yelled angrily as the plane zoomed past his window.

The plane circled down and down and everyone who lived in the Faraway Tree came out of their homes to watch.

Dame Washalot dropped her washing bowl and the water drenched Mr Watzisname. The passengers in the plane laughed happily.

And when the plane landed, everyone tumbled out. Fran fell in a heap on the grass.

"Well," she said, "you can keep the Land of Take-What-You-Want. Give me the Land of Glad-To-Be-Back, any day!"

SEVEN POETS

Hugh MacDiarmid, Norman MacCaig,
Iain Crichton Smith, George Mackay Brown,
Robert Garioch, Sorley MacLean,
Edwin Morgan

with Paintings and Drawings by Alexander Moffat
and Photographs by Jessie Ann Matthew

Third Eye Centre (Glasgow) Ltd
1981

Published March 1981

100 clothbound numbered copies signed by Norman MacCaig, Iain Crichton Smith, George Mackay Brown, Robert Garioch, Sorley MacLean, Edwin Morgan and Alexander Moffat.
ISBN 0 906474 14 0

1900 ordinary copies (card cover)
ISBN 0 906474 13 2

Third Eye Centre acknowledges the financial assistance of the Scottish Arts Council in the publication of this volume

Edited and designed by Christopher Carrell (Third Eye Centre)
Editorial Assistant: Alice Bain (Third Eye Centre)
Published by Third Eye Centre (Glasgow) Ltd., and E. Peterson Ltd., South Shields
Printed by E. Peterson Ltd., 12 Laygate, South Shields, Tyne and Wear
Distributed by Third Eye Centre (Glasgow) Ltd.,
350 Sauchiehall Street, Glasgow G2 3JD. 041-332 7521
Third Eye Centre is grant aided by the Scottish Arts Council, Strathclyde Regional and Glasgow District Councils

Contents

The following poems are published for the first time. **Norman MacCaig:** Rewards and Furies; 19th Floor Nightmare, New York; Christmas Tree; Leaders of Men. **Iain Crichton Smith:** Self-portrait; Islander; Accident Prone; Near Oban; Childhood and Adulthood; The Ghost; Problem. **George Mackay Brown:** William and Mareon Clark; A Man Between Two Hills: Culloden; Hamnavoe Market; Uranium. **Robert Garioch:** The Guid Faimly. **Sorley MacLean:** Eaglais Chatharra (A Church Militant); Iadhshlat (Honeysuckle); Dàn ('Poem' by John Cornford). **Edwin Morgan:** Eve and Adam; 'In a Convex Mirror,' Etc.

Acknowledgements

Acknowledgements are due to the following for permission to reprint poems:
Norman MacCaig (Hogarth Press) *The Equal Skies* 1980, *Riding Lights* 1955. **Iain Crichton Smith** (Gollancz) *Selected Poems* 1970. **George Mackay Brown** (Hogarth Press) *Fishermen with Ploughs* 1971, *Loaves and Fishes* 1959, *Winterfold* 1976. **Robert Garioch** (Macdonald Publishers) *Collected Poems* 1980, (Robert Garioch) Buchanan's *Jephthah* and *The Baptist* 1959. **Sorley MacLean** (Canongate) *Spring tide and Neap tide* 1977. **Edwin Morgan** (Edinburgh University Press) *The Second Life* 1968, (Carcanet) *The New Divan* 1977, (Ian McKelvie) *Instamatic Poems* 1972.

The biographical details and selected publications section for each poet has been compiled by **Hamish Whyte** (Mitchell Library, Glasgow).

The *Six Poets* interviews were edited from the video tape soundtracks by **Marshall Walker**.

Alexander Moffat's paintings of the seven Scottish poets were commissioned by the Scottish Arts Council in 1978.

Foreword

Seven Poets is published to complement the exhibition of portrait paintings and related drawings by Alexander Moffat of the poets featured in this book, which opens at Third Eye Centre on February 20th, 1981 before travelling to galleries throughout the United Kingdom. The paintings and drawings which comprise the exhibition are here shown as illustrations. Also included are seven photographs of the poets by Jessie Ann Matthew, selected from a group of portraits commissioned from her by Third Eye Centre. These were taken during September 1980, with the exception of the photographs of Hugh MacDiarmid which date from shortly before his death in 1978. The photographs will be shown with Alexander Moffat's exhibition at Third Eye Centre, and for the duration of its tour.

To add a further dimension for visitors to the two exhibitions, six colour video tapes were also made in September 1980 by Aidanvision Studios, Carlisle, in association with Third Eye Centre. They feature interviews with and readings by Norman MacCaig, Iain Crichton Smith, George Mackay Brown, Robert Garioch, Sorley MacLean and Edwin Morgan. The poets were filmed at home and in their immediate surroundings; each tape is devoted to a single poet and is a self contained programme lasting approximately twenty-five minutes. The interviewer for the series was Marshall Walker, and the interviews printed in this book are edited from the video sound tracks. All the related *Seven Poets* projects have received financial assistance from the Scottish Arts Council.

The making of *Seven Poets* has been made possible through the hard work and enthusiasm of a number of people. I would particularly like to thank: Norman MacCaig, Iain Crichton Smith, George Mackay Brown, Robert Garioch, Sorley MacLean and Edwin Morgan for giving such positive support to all the proposals submitted to them, enduring so calmly the ensuing demands made of them and offering such warm welcomes to the critic, photographer and film crew who descended upon them in September; I am also extremely grateful for their generous contribution of additional poems, many of which are previously unpublished: Marshall Walker, until recently a Lecturer in American and English Literature at Glasgow University and since January 1981 Professor of English at the University of Waikato in Hamilton, New Zealand; he not only undertook a rigorous ten day tour of Scotland to meet and interview the six poets for the video tape series, but subsequently spent most of his final Christmas in Glasgow working until the early hours editing the interviews for this book when, at very short notice, additional funds made possible their inclusion: Neal Ascherson and Timothy Hyman who gave generously of their time and support: Hamish Whyte (Mitchell Library, Glasgow) for undertaking, with such willingness, further research and enquiry, in addition to his meticulous compilation of the biographical and bibliographical information which accompanies the edited interviews: Roy Thompson, Director of Aidanvision Studios and his team, for making possible the video tape series, and working so hard to ensure its completion.

With the exception of *Poets' Pub,* the paintings by Alexander Moffat reproduced in this book as colour plates are in the collection of the Scottish Arts Council and were completed by the artist with the help and advice of the following former and present staff of the Scottish Arts Council; William Buchanan, Alexander Dunbar, Dr. Isobel Johnstone, Philip Wright and Lindsay Gordon. To all of them Alexander Moffat extends his thanks. The artist is also indebted to Peter de Francia, Timothy Hyman, R. B. Kitaj and Sandra Fisher, Neal Ascherson and Helen Bellany for their whole-hearted support and encouragement throughout the painting of the portraits; and to the late Tom Scott and his son, Jim, for photographing all the paintings and drawings included in this book.

Christopher Carrell (Editor)
Director, Third Eye Centre

Poets' Pub (1980)
left to right: *Norman MacCaig, Sorley MacLean, Hugh MacDiarmid, Iain Crichton Smith, George Mackay Brown, Sydney Goodsir Smith, Edwin Morgan, Robert Garioch. Alan Bold in foreground*
Oil on canvas, 72 × 96 inches

Archie Hind (1968)
Oil on hardboard, 48 × 36 inches
Collection: Archie Hind

Alexander Moffat

Interviewed by Timothy Hyman

How did the commission come about?
I'd already painted a number of writers, but all were personal friends: Alan Bold, Alan Jackson, Pete Morgan, Archie Hind the Glasgow novelist; and my portrait of Norman MacCaig had become quite well-known. But it was Peter de Francia who made a very serious suggestion that I should paint that specific generation of Scottish poets. I think his actual words were "Before it's too late." Every time we met he would ask "How's MacDiarmid getting on? Is he in hospital?" He knew about Sorley MacLean, one or two others. He knew it was a unique phenomenon. He'd say "You'd think the Arts Council up there . . . in a small country . . . It would be a wonderful commission, a wonderful thing to do; and you're the man to do it. Why don't you?" It was just a little while after that, the Scottish Arts Council wrote to me about a scheme for 'Art for Public Places', and I said I didn't have any particular idea for a great mural, but there was one thing I'd like to do which was Scottish and public, in a sense; and that would be to paint a series of portraits of the poets. And that went down extremely well.

Did you have a precedent in mind?
The only one I can think of is the literary portraits of Munch, though my two favourite literary portraits are the Degas pictures in Edinburgh and Glasgow—the portraits of Diego Martelli and of Duranty. I've studied both these pictures for years now.

Do you feel there really is a common ground between these seven poets?
On one level, it's obviously Hugh MacDiarmid. All the others are indebted to him in one way or another. But there's also a kind of Scottish identity they all have, a passionate concern about Scottish history and culture, about its past and its future. These poets have played the leading role, both in their verse and prose in shaping the artistic conscience of this country.

Your setting of the portraits tends to confirm the idea of Scotland as a nation not of cities, but of mountains and lochs?

Hugh MacDiarmid with **Alexander Moffat**
at the opening of the *John Heartfield* exhibition,
New 57 Gallery, Edinburgh 1970.

Hugh MacDiarmid and Neal Ascherson (1978-79)
Pastel and charcoal on paper, 19½ x 26 inches

This is because most of the poets no longer live in the cities and I think this is now true of England as well. It would have been wrong to have placed the poets in cityscapes. The paintings of the Gaelic poets attempt to show the barrenness of the Highlands; there's nothing there now, because the people have been cleared out. One of the things I would hope to have done in the series, is to have made some statement about modern Scotland, about 20th Century Scotland as a whole.

Tell me about the MacDiarmid picture.
Did you already know him?
I first met MacDiarmid in 1962, when he celebrated his seventieth birthday. He still came into Edinburgh now and again; Alan Bold was editing the University literary magazine *Gambit,* and would beg a few little articles or poems. We saw quite a bit of him and his influence was immense. Later, in 1970, I got him to open the John Heartfield exhibition at the Festival and we corresponded a lot at that time. By the time I saw him again in June 1978, he'd had in the previous nine months something like nine hideous operations. The body had gone, but the brain was still very, very active. I went down to Brownsbank with Neal Ascherson and I drew them for a couple of hours as they talked. He reminisced very interestingly about his early life, about Stalin, and about the current fate of the Scottish National Party. He was very keen on the idea of the portraits, though there was lots of good-natured banter about the other poets; like when I said I'd be tackling Sorley MacLean, "Oh, there's not much to paint there".

Did he pose for you?
He wasn't very self-conscious about it. His wife Valda said "You should put your false teeth in, Chris." But he said "Oh no, no, no, Sandy can do that; an artist can always do things like that."

Can I ask you about the precise symbolism of the picture?
I wanted the picture to be about MacDiarmid's dream for Scotland. Many of the figures relate to the Soviet Revolution. That was a crucial event for MacDiarmid; that and his association with the Scottish socialist revolutionary John MacLean, who's just emerging by the side of MacDiarmid's chair. You can make out Lenin, of course, and Mayakovsky; and a bit of Tatlin's tower. I see the landscape behind as symbolising Scotland; it moves from

Sorley MacLean (1978)
Pastel on coloured paper
19½ × 15¼ inches

the lowlands right up into the Shetlands where MacDiarmid lived in the 1930's. I hope I can get through to a lot of people with this painting.

And the settings for the other portraits?
The Crichton Smith landscape is an evocation of Lewis, his birthplace, in the Outer Hebrides; the desolation symbolising again the forcible removal of people from the islands which these Gaelic poets still feel intensely. Sorley MacLean is one of the great oral historians of the Western Islands. He can talk for hours about the way the Highlanders have been ruthlessly exploited over the past 200 years or so, tracing with ease the individual involvement of families—fathers, grandfathers, great grandfathers, etc.—in historical events.

But the peat-digging figures are present-day, not historical?
Yes. But I had the idea of painting him with historical figures; for example, the Battle of the Braes which took place in Skye only a few miles from the poet's house, at the end of the nineteenth century. It could be something I'll do in the future.

With MacCaig and Morgan the setting seems less obviously symbolic?
I didn't want to put MacCaig in a Sutherland setting as that would have meant too many landscapes. He had to be in Edinburgh, in my studio again as he was in my 1968 portrait. But I also have a plan for a picture of MacCaig and MacDiarmid in Princes Street; I want this to be about our 'Romantic toun'. I've tried to represent Eddie Morgan not only as a poet, but as a professor and critic; the Paolozzi print, the Modernist chair, are literally there in his study. I've used these items to pay tribute to his surrealism and his use of scientific imagery.

And the Garioch setting . . ?
The Garioch painting was the first of the series. I had to begin with a poet in his study . . .

When you went to Orkney to see George Mackay Brown was that your first visit?
Yes, that was my first trip to Orkney although George Mackay Brown and I are old friends. In fact we were students in Edinburgh at the same time and we met regularly in the Rose Street bars. We

George Mackay Brown (1980)
Charcoal and pastel on pink paper
21¾ × 14¾ inches

had a great reunion with endless cups of strong tea, chocolate biscuits, and the occasional mug of home-brewed ale. I suggested to George that I had an idea for a big painting of all the poets together in Milne's Bar and he was very enthusiastic. "My, that's a wonderful painting you have in mind, Sandy". And I thought "I've got to do this now."

Do you have a particular setting for the big group portrait? Who is the central figure?
In this painting I've attempted to evoke the romance of Edinburgh's Bohemian life of the late 1950's and early 1960's (when I came on the scene). The poets are together in a space suggesting Milne's, the Abbotsford and the Cafe Royal, the so-called 'poets' pubs'. The main figure is that of Sydney Goodsir Smith who died before the series got underway. I think all of the others would have wanted Sydney to be the central figure; he was *the* great character of all the poets and wrote many fine verses about Edinburgh pub life.

"Grieve and Garioch aye tuim their pints . . .
While lean MacCaig stauns snuffin the western seas
And Brown leads wi his Viking chin . . ."

I don't want them to be *too* drunk in my painting though.

What would you say has been the most valuable aspect of this commission?
I've been able to come to terms with Scotland much more. Just travelling around, with this specific task in mind (meeting these Gaels for example, going over to the Hebrides, down to Biggar, up to Orkney) I've really embraced the whole of Scotland. It's made me think for the first time in my life really seriously about certain aspects of Scottish life, of Scottish history. And meeting and becoming friends with the poets, that's pretty special.

What do you think made you a painter?
In one way, it was just the gifted little boy; at 15 you specialise and art was one of my subjects. But I think the turning point was being taken by my Art teacher to a Festival exhibition, the Moltzau Collection. That was the first time I'd seen Modern painting; Picasso, Braque, Matisse, Bonnard, lots of Abstract painting . . . That was it. I became a fanatic about painting.

Works by **Alexander Moffat** (left) and **John Bellany** (right) displayed on the railings outside the Royal Scottish Academy during the 1965 Edinburgh Festival; a pamphlet by **Alan Bold** attacking the R.S.A. was handed out to passers-by.

This photograph hung in Milne's Bar for several years.

MacDiarmid, and I think all the other poets, reacted strongly against English language, against English tradition. Did you?
Yes. But I was reacting against the watered-down French tradition of the Academy as well. I looked to a Northern tradition. There was Breughel, Durer, Cranach, Grunewald, Rembrandt. Munch and Beckmann came later. Oddly enough, Goya then seemed to me a 'Northern Artist'. Spanish and Northern European Art have much in common of course, including a special feeling for expressionism.

Why do you think poetry has flourished in Scotland so much more than painting, these fifty years? When you hear Josef Herman speak of Glasgow in the 1940's, it's clear many painters were in the circle of MacDiarmid . . .
The painters—their horizons, their ideas, you can't really compare them. J. D. Fergusson was a good painter (Herman calls him "Britain's leading Cézannist"). But in his paintings he stuck mainly to still-lives and nudes. A very limited subject-matter. You don't get anyone in Scotland painting about the sort of things Sorley MacLean for example wrote about—The Spanish Civil War, Love Affairs, the Clearances . . . that's unknown in Scottish 20th Century painting.

Was that the sort of thing that you and John Bellany used to talk about?
That was more or less our platform—that something had happened in Scottish poetry which hadn't in painting. That poetry seemed to *matter* and that painting was for the bourgeois living-room, little pieces of decoration, specially framed . . .

Are there contemporary portraits you admire?
I have a soft spot for Kitaj's double portrait of John Golding and James Joll. Also Peter de Francia's portrait of Salvatore Quasimodo, the Sicilian poet. And I've a great respect for Hockney, but it would be difficult to apply his neo-classical style to the Scottish scene. There's a kind of raw romance that exists here, and if you didn't have that you'd be missing 75% of what I find in Scottish life. But my favourite portraits all come from the first half of this century—Picasso, Kokoschka, Beckmann, Dix, Balthus . Art since 1945 has turned away from the human face

Hugh MacDiarmid (1978)
Pastel on light brown coloured paper
19¾ × 14⅝ inches

with the most trivial of consequences. Beckmann's statement "The elimination of the human component from artistic representation is the cause of the vacuum which makes us all suffer in varying degrees . . ." has always been my credo.

The kind of collage-composition you use in the MacDiarmid picture is probably unimaginable without Kitaj; and don't you think the kind of line you've employed in the last few years (a smoother, slower line than Beckmann's, or than your own used to be) and this dry way of putting on paint . . ?
Yes, all that owes something to R.B., there's no doubt about that. I can speak to Kitaj for half an hour, or read one of his little essays, and I feel completely inspired; I feel "it's worthwhile doing this after all". It's important to be inspired by others, to create an atmosphere of hope, as it were. *The Human Clay* exhibition, both his introduction and his whole ideal, was something I was totally in sympathy with; taking a stand, making a polemic out of the human thing.

Do you think your interest in music has interlocked with your painting?
Yes, I think there's been a definite merging. I look upon certain aspects of my painting in musical terms. I would say that nowadays my colour is more 'Straussian'—this idea of sensuous orchestration. I was against Strauss ten years ago, thinking him superficial in comparison with Mahler or Berg. Now I can see that, in simple terms, Strauss was more concerned with beauty than truth. I've been influenced a little by this. I suppose I'm searching for a more subtle art.

What about poetry?
Brecht as a poet has always been a particular favourite, and Wallace Stevens, who MacCaig introduced me to. Heine and Rilke are wonderful poets. And there's Ezra Pound, who MacCaig warned me about, he was always a man to read.

I partly see MacDiarmid's role as having put Pound into Scots. Even the tone of voice . . .
Oh, of course. MacDiarmid was always involved in polemic, changing the world, challenging provincialism. I found all of that very attractive when I was younger, less so now. Both Pound and MacDiarmid wanted to write long ambitious poems, to combine the lyric and the epic; that greatly appeals to me.

Berliners III (1978)
Oil on canvas, 47 × 74 inches
Private collection: New York

Neal Ascherson (left) with **Alexander Moffat** in the artist's studio, 1979

You don't feel inadequate about your own lack of prophetic fire?
No. You see I used to think it was absolutely essential to be some kind of 'committed person' in a political sense. Then I suddenly woke up one day and realised it wasn't; I realised there were greater things than simple political ideologies. I wanted to create more than an art of protest. Bonnard wasn't protesting, was he? Perhaps painting is ill-suited to the prophetic, writing being the true medium of the prophet. Anyway, I've become wary of political prophets. I made a journey to Buchenwald in the sixties with Bold and Bellany. There I saw what could happen when extreme ideologies become reality. I remain 'committed' to social justice; I'm still an idealist.

Do you think yours is now an ironic stance? In the portrait of MacDiarmid for instance?
No. I think the *Hymn to Lenin* is genuine; everything there I like. The picture is a straight-forward homage, a labour of love.

In your series of three large paintings entitled Berliners, *you portray the journalist Neal Ascherson in the midst of Ulricke Meinhof and other political extremists; his role is a witness, almost a voyeur. Do you think it's over-interpreting to suggest this constellation says something about your own stance towards ideology, towards life.*
The *Berliners* paintings were my first figure paintings after a series of highly subjective landscapes. In many ways they are the most objective of all my paintings.
This may be because they are about a journalist. I admire the journalist's sense of reality, his dedication, his involvement in epoch-making events, and the disciplined way he distances himself from those events in his attempts to write truthfully. Yes, I think these qualities are useful for the artist. Paradoxically, Neal Ascherson is a highly subjective writer; maybe that's why I value his writing and his friendship.

What is it you admire so much about Thomas Mann?
It's the sense of humanity moving on an epic scale, but at the same time looking into the individual.

But in Doctor Faustus *Mann deals with the* 'subject-matter' *of Ex-*

Alan Bold (1969)
Drawing, 20 × 15 inches

pressionism, only to distance it with this terribly ironic voice.
Yes, but why should one just rush into everything? This is a wonderful method that Mann used. You've got to remember that everyone around him was rushing in.

You like his lack of passion?
I wouldn't put it like that. You see, I greatly admire Munch; I think he's absolutely wonderful. But then I greatly admire Raphael, who is an overwhelmingly rational and intellectual artist. And I love Poussin. It's this problem of reconciling—Busoni's idea—reinventing a genuine contemporary classicism, instead of doing what Stravinsky did, revamping ancient music.

Do you think you're not only a humanist, you're also a bit of a rationalist?
I've never been religious which probably accounts for my attitudes towards abstraction. But this isn't to say that I am totally opposed to the irrational and to abstraction in art. German Expressionism, an irrational movement, has had a profound effect on my painting. I suppose that's my own personal dilemma, a series of contradictions with which, like many artists, I have to live.

In your earlier portraits, there were no props?
No, they were mostly plain backgrounds. Some people were critical at the time, saying "You've got to get some books in", all those kind of corny things. In those days I hated that idea, I wanted to strip painting down to a rawness, an essential statement. I didn't want anything coming between the figure and the emotion expressed in the painting. I didn't want these 'little bits'.

But do you still think everything is really there in the face?
Yes, I do believe that. These elaborate settings are probably peculiar to this series.

Have you enjoyed making them?
I have, tremendously. But I've had the time, the luxury of attempting it. It was almost as if I had a now or never chance to see what could be done. I could have painted the series so much quicker if it had been just faces. But the point is to produce a painting that is a work of art and not just a superficial likeness of someone; you could do that in half an hour.

Robert Garioch (1978)
Oil on canvas, 23 × 16 inches

Do you feel qualities are lost between the direct drawing made on the spot, and the full-scale canvas, back in the studio?
I think perhaps that everything gets lost; and then you've just got to struggle to get it back again. But drawing and the finished painting are different things. The great French masters of last century would draw and collect notes in the summer months and during the winter they would create their huge 'machines' back in the studio. Painting takes time. On the other hand I think I've sometimes ruined pictures by imposing some idea of 'finish'; pictures have simply died a death. I'd like to be able to make a painting like a drawing; that would be a long-cherished ambition. To have all the elements one has in drawing, the spontaneity, the vigour; at the same time the sense of design. Lautrec did this—he's often in my thoughts.

These portraits are peculiarly objective; there's very little sense of your having a relationship with the sitter. The figures are set apart.
Edward Gage wrote of my earlier portraits that "the overwhelming impression was one of smouldering emotion set in realist drabness". The drabness has gone now and I've distanced myself from the overt emotion of my earlier pictures. What interests me in Expressionist art—Munch, Kirchner, Beckmann—is not exactly their subjectivity but the forcing of the human condition into the centre of one's vision. This absolute preoccupation with humanity, from the individual right through to the social; examining themselves, at the same time examining the crowd. If you insist on total subjectivity, then you've got to hope people are tuned into your peculiar temperament. But I think that art's a much greater, more autonomous business than that. If we take a truly universal artist like Beethoven or Rembrandt, I don't think that we have to be in any way peculiar to appreciate their art. At the same time no one could claim that their art lacked in intensity. They were concerned with expressing 'ideas', not with themselves. They achieved a harmony between 'the idea' and their own individuality as artists and that would be my ideal. I've no wish to make any sensational show of temperament in my work; only to make people more aware of, and so perhaps enrich, the life around them. I would like people to contemplate my paintings; to come back again and again.

Hugh MacDiarmid (Hymn to Lenin) (1979)
Oil on canvas, 44½ × 74¾ inches

Seven Poets
by Neal Ascherson

Introduction
Part One

Here are the portraits of seven Scottish poets. Six are living; one is lately dead. None of them is young, and all are well established and in varying degrees well published. Their reputation is equally strong outwith Scotland; most of their readers live either south of the Border or in the wider English-reading world, exception made for Robert Garioch who writes mainly in Scots and has published less than the others, and for Sorley MacLean, who can reach most of his audience only through translations from his Gaelic.

Why this particular seven? There are other poets of such stature in Scotland whose work and likenesses are not here. The answer must lie with the painter, Sandy Moffat. He did not choose the seven because of their looks (although Norman MacCaig is a beautiful man), nor because they had 'interesting' faces. He sought them out because their work has moved him, instructed and formed him. A painter with a poet for subject is not disclosing inner truths about the sitter, or switching on an x-ray which reveals how his verses nestle in the bush of his eyebrow or the knee of his trousers. He is using physical appearance to focus and get on canvas aspects of his own reflections and inquiries—like a child doing a drawing who demands "something to press on". In the same way, there's nothing of some literary competition in Moffat's choice. These are not necessarily 'the greatest', although one—MacDiarmid—is gigantic beyond the scale of other Scottish poets.

To read again the work of these seven is to be aware that the 'Scottish Renaissance' is over and done with. It is not dead, but part of the past. That movement, of which MacDiarmid was the prime mover, did not only create a poetry in Scots—artificial and eclectic, in MacDiarmid's case, or genuinely vernacular as in Garioch's verse. It was a sort of college, demanding, sometimes eccentric, often echoing with terrible rows, whose legacy is both its own body of verse and (more important,) a fundamental confidence available to Scottish poets whichever of the three national languages they work in and however little they feel they have to do with the Dunbar-Henryson-Fergusson tradition upon which the Renaissance insisted. The need to assert 'Scottishness' no longer gnaws at the writer. For the two out of these seven who write only in English, MacCaig and Mackay Brown, the relationship to English poetry in the rest of the world is easy and fraternal as it could not have been without the twenty-five years of the Renaissance. Garioch remains a living part of that movement. MacLean was deeply influenced by it, both politically and in his taste, and performed for Gaelic literature the re-establishment of traditions and norms which the Renaissance achieved in Scots.

Escaped from college, graduates do not usually do what their teachers expected of them. It was hoped, even assumed, that the literary revival would fuse naturally with a political revival. This did not really happen. The European pattern of cultural nationalism, with the poet on the barricade and the lexicographer of the national language elected president of the new republic, was not repeated in Scotland. It is instructive that none of these seven, except for Iain Crichton Smith, signed up actively with the Scottish resurgence of nationalism in the seventies. A guarded sympathy was evoked; some voted SNP; some pronounced for self-government but with reservations (in the case of MacDiarmid and MacLean, wanting something more radical and bold); some stayed quiet and watched. Superficially, and to the surprise of intelligent foreign visitors in those years, it looked as if Scottish culture was dissolving at the very moment that Scottish political awareness was growing harder and more formidable.

The disjuncture was real: the impression of decline was false. The false impression came mostly from Edinburgh, where the band of writers and admirers who had gathered so conspicuously in the Rose Street pubs had at last broken up. Poetry was becoming more decentralised. Of these living six, only two remain in Edinburgh: Glasgow, Skye, Orkney and Oban claim the others. The disjuncture from politics, on the other hand, springs from something which concerns all these poets: the shattered nature of Scottish

Hugh MacDiarmid (1978)
Charcoal and pastel on paper, 15 × 20 inches

consciousness, which isn't a low, flat floor of peasant culture on which all stand together but a wild junk-yard of high-culture fragments, English imports, oral traditions of 'the Scots commons' and proletarian 'socialist realism' from the thirties. If one is to say that there's something Scottish about all Moffat's subjects beyond their birth, it is the sense of duty to bring some order into the junk-yard which united them all. Several happen to be teachers, but most could claim to be educators, even cultural missionaries. MacDiarmid, MacLean and George Mackay Brown have all constructed ordered landscapes (Scotland, Skye in Gaelic Scotland, Orkney of the Vikings) in which to set their poems. Most curious and significant of all, there is the passion to translate. MacDiarmid translated, sometimes more imperious than accurate, from Russian, German, French and Gaelic; Garioch from French, German, Latin, Greek and Italian; Morgan from at least six languages (not counting putting Shakespeare into Scots); Crichton Smith from his own and others' Gaelic. Consciously or unconsciously, they here respond to the twin warnings of the old literary nationalists: Scotland is divided within itself, and Scotland's natural connection to the European mainland has been almost blocked.

MacDiarmid has gone—gone where, one cannot quite be sure. He always conveyed a sense of interstellar travel in his work, not only in his reaching towards the inanimate, his telling-over of the names of stones and stars, but in his intellectual voyaging towards understanding so distant and ultimate that he could sometimes be tracked rather than followed. He was buried in Langholm, his birthplace, in 1978 when he was 86 years old. He never got to hold the final two-volume collection of his poems in his hands; delayed by this and that, it missed him by a few months.

He was a voluminous writer. Not all he wrote was good—he used to say that he was a volcano throwing out some fire and a great deal of rubbish— but by the end of his life it was seen that he was the last of the giants of early twentieth-century poetry, a peer of Yeats and Pound. MacDiarmid's range was vast, from the early lyrics in Scots through the Scots intellectual epic of *A Drunk Man Looks at the Thistle* to the long, sere, 'scientific' poems of the thirties and later. But his poetic greed was even vaster. MacDiarmid seemed to eat dictionaries and encyclopaedias for breakfast; sometimes the reader is tumbled off down an avalanche of looted words, half-digested geology and linguistics, whole chunks of text lifted from other writers. He wrote almost nothing about the direct human relationships, which has shocked a few critics. But it was usually a human event—a death—which provoked the very best of his short poems. If there is perfection, some of those—*Crystals Like Blood,* or *Of John Davidson*—are perfect.

He destroyed the idea of Scottish literature which he found, and almost single-handed created a new and vigorous sensibility to the past and present which is still dominant. His critical books and essays, and all his magnificent, flaying journalism would fill a long shelf if it were ever to be retrieved and edited. MacDiarmid was a Nationalist and a Communist, expelled from both parties but dying a Communist again, rejoicing in every contradiction and looking forward—with angry impatience—to a red republican Scotland in which (as Tom Nairn put it) the last minister had been strangled with the last copy of the Sunday Post. This man was the father of the modern Scottish imagination, and the six other men in this book and related exhibitions are all in the poetic generation which—plainly or indirectly—owes its life to him.

Norman MacCaig

Part Two

Of the seven, Norman MacCaig is the most sensual poet. The physical world keeps bumping gently into him—a mountain seen, a gannet, a sea-pink, a basking shark. He perceives with an intensity, an energy which might be difficult to bear if he did not lead it off into turning wheels. A delicate mechanism starts to spin; soon the thing perceived is transformed and spliced with intellect and association. What will come out of the process in the end is only MacCaig's guess, and he is too intently at work to guess. One usually ends reading a MacCaig poem—and he is specially skilful at ends—with two sensations arriving at once: a pang of astonishment and a shock of assent.

Norman MacCaig (1979)
Pastel on paper
29 × 22 inches

Norman MacCaig (1979)
Charcoal on paper, 28½ × 21¾ inches

Once he was even more sensual. He used words more splashingly: a less fastidious Norman MacCaig, more of a bounder. This was his 'New Apocalypse' period, mostly in the forties. It's supposed that he deprecates that style now; certainly, none of that verse appears in his latest *Selected Poems,* which go back only to 1955, the year when he made a new, reformed start with the collection *Riding Lights*. All the same, the poems in *Far Cry* (1943) are very much better than he seems to think.

A poet as intelligent as MacCaig is naturally fascinated by his own creative processes. He has often described them, more economically than a critic could, as in *Ego:*—

"... Tree
And star are ways of finding out what I
Mean in a text composed of earth and sky".

In the same poem he discusses the seeing of a rose, a "seeming coloured on the air/With the transparencies which make up me,/Thickened to existence by my notice". MacCaig, then, is not a Romantic, who joyfully obliterates himself in the thing seen, but a metaphysical. It is said that he learned much from Andrew Young, a poet who owed nothing to the Scottish Renaissance but who also wrote from the impulse of the physical thing seen—mountain and loch—with a metaphysical response which is a good deal more reticent than MacCaig's.

His family background is mostly a Gaelic one—Harris—although he has spent much of his life in Edinburgh. His work arises from long, returning sojourns in the northwest, from its forms and creatures. But these are visits; he is not consciously a part of those communities in the way that MacLean or Iain Crichton Smith or George Mackay Brown are still involved in theirs, the sense of old and new injustice inescapably present in their verse whether they wish it or not. MacCaig is far the least political of any of these seven poets; he makes few social comments. His wit, and his own sense of tragedy (which grows more intense these days) seldom play on more than one person at a time. But he is aware of humanity as a tribe; I think of *Celtic Cross* which speaks of

"The tangled generations ravelled out
In links of song whose strong, sweet choruses
Are these stone involutions to the eyes ..."

And it is not only for himself that he has worked. For years he insisted, before the stature of Sorley MacLean was widely recognised, that a major European poet was writing in Gaelic. MacCaig has given friendship and criticism to most of his contemporaries. Hugh MacDiarmid's last word was his first name.

Iain Crichton Smith (1980)
Charcoal on coloured paper, 15 × 21 inches

Iain Crichton Smith

Part Three

This is a tense, unsmiling poetry. Iain Crichton Smith has said for himself that he wants to write a poetry of tensions rather than of statement. But these aren't glittering contradictions, of the sort that MacDiarmid rejoiced in, or MacCaig's silvery paradoxes. These are the tensions of ways out which are blocked, chances seen only when they are past and impossible, choices between bad and worse. He can seize upon instants of pure happiness *(Two Girls Singing),* but they fall like a sudden shower of grace to which man is not entitled. This is a highly Presbyterian poetry.

He was born and brought up in Lewis. Now he lives in Oban, a rather halfway place which has lost most of its Gaelic, neither a rural community nor a Scottish city but a port passed through by people on their way to somewhere else. This too is a tension. It must suit him, for he is, like most of the seven, an astonishingly prolific writer. There are novels and short stories, plays in Gaelic and translations (of Sorley MacLean, among others), and a large body of Gaelic verse. Donald J. Macleod has claimed that his Gaelic poems do not compare with his best English verse, or even with his Gaelic fiction. But Smith's own translations of his Gaelic verse into English suggest something else: that in his first language he achieves a special sharpness and rapidity, but that Gaelic does not permit him the intellectual subtleties and speculation he exploits so movingly in English.

Few poets are more valued by other poets than he. They, and critics, tend to stand round Iain Crichton Smith trying to be helpful: he should take a decision on this, move into a wider world of that. In his latest collection, *In the Middle,* one poem compares critics of poetry to flies feasting on a carcass. This is one of the rare moments when his anger, always to be heard pacing about in the wings, jumps out into the lights. What has become of Gaelic Scotland is a deep hurt in Smith, one focus of the anger; contempt for electronic mass culture is another. But these are no more than places at which the underground fire pierces surface. Smith is outraged at what must happen to a human being who is born and dies, always freshly shocked at how much worse callous people can make this bad job for others: something like that is the burning lake inside him. In general he holds this emotion tightly under control. The sequence *From Bourgeois Land* (1969) scratches a diamond point of irony across the mansion-polished tables of those who think they have life safely locked out. (That tidy Scottish town, where "Gauleiters pace by curtained windows", and "distant Belsen smokes in the calm air"). Smith, although he is a Nationalist, has wondered whether a country as bourgeois as Scotland (in the sense that people are careful not to care too intensely about anything) will ever do anything significant. He once observed, almost with regret, that few Scottish poets had ever gone mad.

His most exciting poem is the long meditation called *Deer on the High Hills.* Written in English, although its tone and some rhythms recall a Gaelic translation, it is a complex and often difficult speculation on image and reality. Edwin Morgan once complained that Smith had lost his way in this poem, or given his problem up as insoluble, but it ends firmly in a statement about the vainness of the poetic effort:

> "There is no metaphor. The stone is stony.
> The deer step out in isolated air.
> We move at random on an innocent journey".

George Mackay Brown

Part Four

This is the least tormented, the most spiritually secure of the seven poets. George Mackay Brown is surrounded by three lines of defence. The first is a moat, the Pentland Firth. Mackay Brown lives in Orkney, at Stromness where he was born. He did go south to Edinburgh and Newbattle Abbey for his studies, but then he went home again. He does not gladly leave the islands, and he seldom writes about anything else.

His second fortification is history. The Vikings held

George Mackay Brown
(1980)
Oil on canvas
60 × 60 inches

Orkney for six hundred years, and in that period, "terrible and fruitful", the islanders played their part in the empire which reached its claws around the edges of Europe from the North Cape to Constantinople. The Orcadians often prefer what Mackay Brown calls "a sentimental make-believe" version of their history, reducing the Viking time especially to stylised wing-hats in long-ships. But this period, and the crofter-fishermen centuries which came afterwards, are the framework in which this poet sets and examines time. He perceives a silly, recent cult of progress which seems to be cutting Orcadians off from the past which alone can give meaning to the present. He celebrates that past, in poem after poem.

The third, inmost ring is his religion. George Mackay Brown is a convert to Catholicism. It's impossible to separate this from his encounter with the greatest of all Orcadian poets, Edwin Muir. It was Muir who was Warden of Newbattle when Mackay Brown went there as a student, and Muir had returned to Christianity in the same way. Both men understood their Orkney as an allegory, standing for an original innocence which no suffering and storm of cruelty could finally violate. The Catholic faith, with its powerful affirmation of the collective and its sacramental view of an organic society and its traditions, provided Mackay Brown with the ideology for his Orcadian world-view.

He likes the concept of ' heraldry ', the source for him of the "archaic, pellucid imagery" in Muir's verse and his own. Heraldry, by which he means all that is a sign to him, even his landscape, "is the fury of history made wise and formal; from its hands we take at last the wholesome images—the heart's bread—that our ancestors sowed for us in passion and blindness". The poet and critic Alexander Scott is one of those who have found fault with this, complaining that Mackay Brown lives in "a mediaeval religious dream" remote from contemporary feeling, and that his religious poems, especially, are too lush and lax. He violently rejects the Reformation as an attempt by outside forces to wreck that heraldry; "Knox brought all down in his wild hogmanay", leaving a vandalised culture: ". . . the thrawn acre where those good stones bleed".

But it would be badly wrong to see Mackay Brown as a mere reactionary. Like all poets with a Highland or island background, he holds the image of the roofless house at his heart, and his anger and regret flow more easily and directly than for a Gaelic writer. He has composed many poems on the theme, none more beautiful than *Dead Fires* with its simple, compelling variations on cold hearth and scattered stones, the abandoned township of Rackwick:—

"The fire beat like a heart in each house
From the first corner-stone
Till they led through the sagging lintel the last old one.
The poor and the good fires are all quenched.
Now, cold angel, keep the valley
From the bedlam and cinders of a Black Pentecost".

Safe behind his three magic rings—water, time and spirit—George Mackay Brown applies his powerful imagination to very various projects. He has written plenty of succesful fiction, and his book *Orkney Tapestry* (1973) is an assortment of Viking and crofter history, folk tales, poetry and drama. He is a rich, confident, colourful writer, appealing successfully to a readership much wider than most contemporary poets can hope for. And yet Mackay Brown's verse is not always simple and direct. The religious work, especially, is dense with allusion and symbol, often hard to decipher; the Viking poems and songs yield more to the reader who has studied his prose versions of saga stories. He is at his very best in his short poems about Orkney in or close to the present, *Love Letter, Unpopular Fisherman,* even the comical *Afternoon Tea.* He may feel that they are slight, compared to much of his work, but their irony and economy—things closely related—display all his art at once.

Robert Garioch
Part Five

This is a town poet. Robert Garioch is one of the last representatives in Europe of an ancient and honourable tribe: a man whose verses mock and celebrate the life and the spectacle of his own city. Edinburgh is an archaic town, and this is an archaic form. It is a place still ruled by its old oligarchy, the poor rubbing up against the rich and

Robert Garioch (1978)
Charcoal on paper
29½ × 21½ inches

laughing at their unchanging round of ceremonies (of which the Festival is one) and of civic scandals, a place where everyone knows everyone.

"The seenil City Faithers, that decoir
Our seignories, hirple in borrowed tiles,
Fu sanctimonious, til historic aisles . . ."

He is an underdog poet, the voice of the exasperated man in the pub rather than of the mythical 'ratepayer',an inveterate biter of well-shod heels. He is an intellectual, but deliberately not one of the 'intelligentsia', one who reserves the right to be at once a man of great literary and musical erudition and the fellow listening at the other end of the bar, with incredulous contempt, to "the cognoscenti/a hie-brou clan, ilk wi a beard on him". Garioch's Edinburgh isn't even the modern city. He is a poet of the Old Town, where all classes and conditions once lived packed together on the same stair, before the New Town arose and drew off the middle classes to "whar classie Queen Street and Drumsheugh/nou stand sae snod".

His literary ancester is Robert Fergusson, the Edinburgh eighteenth-century poet who died young and mad and left behind him the most brilliant of all Scottish urban poetry. Garioch's ode to Fergusson claims him as a predecessor: "monie an airt/formed us in common, faur apairt/in time, but fell alike in hert". But this poem also praises the authenticity of the Scots in which Fergusson wrote, a genuine Edinburgh speech far less eclectic than the Scots used by Burns (who supplemented his Ayrshire vocabulary from all over Lowland Scotland). The compliment can be returned to Garioch; more than any of the Renaissance writers in 'braid Scots', Robert Garioch uses a real local language which can still be encountered. He is an extraordinary master of poetic form, relishing the two old metres of 'standard Habbie' and of 'Christ's Kirk on the Green', but the sharps and flats of Edinburgh talk are part of the architecture of his lighter verse. It would be strange to hear them read by a Glaswegian.

But there is something disingenuous about Garioch's pose as a sharp-tongued man of the people. For all his claim to be Fergusson's child, Garioch is vastly more learned and sophisticated than Fergusson ever was. He is not just a city satirist and poet of the passing scene, but also a writer working in the tradition of the Scottish Renaissance which found universal themes in Scotland and sought to make this small country's damaged language a universal medium. In his long poem *The Muir,* Garioch clambers about the peaks of speculation, reflecting on the nature of perception and the metaphysics of atomic theory. Like MacDiarmid, he relies here on the spark struck when Scots, with its tough precision about things touched and seen, bangs against the abstract. *The Muir,* strange as it seems at first, is one of the most successful poems in modern Scots. Where MacDiarmid, in his 'scientific' poetry, seems at times to be merely bashing technical terminology with a Scots dictionary, Garioch in *The Muir* is always at ease with his language, a Fergusson who has been to college.

And Garioch is a great translator. He has translated from French and German, from the Greek of Hesiod and the Latin of George Buchanan. Next to Fergusson, his closest forbear has turned out to be the nineteenth-century Roman poet Giuseppe Belli (also a town poet, using Roman dialect to mock his City Faithers and give a voice to the anger of the poor), and Garioch has put dozens of the *Roman Sonnets* into Scots. He has even done a few versions from Gaelic, and it's worth saying about a man who seems to be such a loner that it was Garioch's efforts (and, it's said, his own money) which produced the first publication of Sorley MacLean's work.

Garioch fell rather quiet in recent years, but then ambushed a wide audience with some work in English. *Two Men and a Blanket,* a prose memoir about his life as a prisoner of war, came out a few years ago, and Radio Forth cleverly appointed him their poet laureate. Garioch squibs jump out of the aether, causing high-heid-yins to miss the gears of their Volvos and encouraging disaffection. Robert Garioch may be the latest in his poetic lineage, but the vigour and bite of his verse suggests that he may not be the last.

Left: **Sorley MacLean** (1978)
Brown conté on white paper
16½ × 11 inches

Right: **Sorley MacLean** (1979)
Oil on canvas
60 × 36 inches

Sorley MacLean (Somhairle MacGill-Eain)

Part Six

This is the most original Gaelic poet of his century. Many who read his work set him among the most gifted and powerful poets writing in any European language. Even for that majority of MacLean's readers who have no Gaelic, the judgement is easy to accept. A translation is a fossil, giving the shape of the creature in a new material which is at once a fresh mind and another tongue. But in the case of MacLean, there have been several translators and one of them is MacLean himself—not, it is asserted by some scholars, the most faithful to his own Gaelic original. All this lights up the Gaelic text in a helpful perspective. The cycle of love poems, *Dàin do Eimhir,* is a good example. It is easy to get hold of a full verse translation done by Iain Crichton Smith, and of Sorley MacLean's own rendering into English of at least some of them, facing the Gaelic. Armed with two books, and with an elementary notion of how to pronounce Gaelic (for MacLean is the most expert craftsman in sound), a respectable attempt to appreciate MacLean can be made.

The first thing to strike such a reader will be the intensity of MacLean's personal agony. Much of the poetry, especially the longer pieces like *Hallaig* or the tremendous *The Woods of Raasay,* uses the Gaelic-classical background of much older writing: that brilliant, enamelled landscape of sea, hill, red rowan and dun deer which is as springy and formal as the decoration of an Iron Age shield. But against that background moves a human being of our own time and sensibility, tormented by love, appalled and seized by political events taking place far beyond the tall fence of the Cuillins. This is a twentieth-century poet, learned in Gaelic literature but also in English metaphysical verse and touched by the spirit of the Scottish Renaissance (which he encountered at Edinburgh University fifty years ago). He grew up in a time when Gaelic literature seemed to be narrowing to its end, and—through his own writing rather than through any organised

movement—gave Gaelic poetry in the space of a few years an entirely new sense of its capacity and adaptability, and a world-wide range of awareness which it hardly ever attained in the past.

Dàin do Eimhir, which appeared in 1943, has been called the cornerstone of this Gaelic revival. By then, the formative events in MacLean's life were over. In the early thirties, his own knowledge of Skye's land-leaguing struggle against social injustice combined with the slump and the rise of Fascism to make a Marxist of him, although—unlike MacDiarmid—he never joined the Communist Party. Neither did he follow his heart and go to fight in Spain. We don't know precisely why: MacLean speaks only of "difficult family circumstances" which kept him at home, but regret and remorse for that failure were to become a primary colour in his verse. MacLean's other wound (he does offer evidence for those who still think that literature arises from an injury, like the oyster's pearl) was in love. Here again, about all we are allowed to know about this is in the marvellous *Dàin do Eimhir* sequence, MacLean referring seldom and unwillingly to a "terrible personal experience" in December 1939 which blocked one channel of his poetry—the long, political medley-poem *An Cuilithionn* (The Cuillin), never completed—and opened another. All the pain and the tensions of his political and emotional disasters began to work together, asking questions and dissolving certainties. ". . . Her beauty cast a film/over poverty and a bitter wound/and over the world of Lenin's intellect . . ." His respect for the Soviet Union began to diminish, after the Warsaw Rising of 1944, and a less dogmatic socialism emerged, always tinged with his own rather pessimistic nationalism (". . . the feebleness of our dismal Scotland").

To write in what is still, for all the efforts made, a dying language is an experience difficult for other poets to imagine—but not only a negative one. The very weakness of the contemporary Gaelic literature he found gave MacLean licence to innovate and revive as he chose. The theme of the "roofless house" and the vanished ancestors is naturally present to him '*(Hallaig,* the best-known example), but the final impression isn't one of cultural despair. The vigour and passion of MacLean's work, his harmony of symbols and sound, and his complete success in developing a poetry which makes a symphony of ideas almost without the use of an abstract word make him the most important poet working in Scotland today.

Edwin Morgan

Part Seven

"Science is a cure for science; technology is a cure for technology". Edwin Morgan is a restlessly clever man who has no inhibitions about his delight in his own times. There are few experiments in contemporary poetry which he has not tried, often—as in his concrete poetry—achieving rapid mastery in a new field. The world around him seems to be a constant challenge, as if he feared above all that poetry would become essentially a nostalgic, backward-looking form of expression. Morgan insists that what is novel is not therefore 'trendy'; the astronaut, he once argued, undergoes an experience which is human and "somehow you feel that there must be a way of expressing these experiences in poetry". Science fiction, the movies, the scenes of his native Glasgow, the technological vocabulary all fascinate him.

A poet like this runs some risk of being dismissed as a sort of versifying journalist, a writer who selects 'likely' themes and new literary fashions and then exploits his talents to illustrate them. That is never true of Morgan, although his addiction to the work of the 'beat' poets aroused some growls and although his powers are sometimes outstripped by his enthusiasm (as in the strange, long poem *The Whittrick*). His versatility is dazzling, but almost never superficial, and it comes from overflowing learning and curiosity rather than from any personal ambition to be out front.

Mere trendiness would have drawn him away from a Scottish poetic identity. But Edwin Morgan accepts this identity, with a deliberate lack of fuss or drama. The important things here are, first, to have got over the compulsion to emphasize Scottishness and—as he used to put it—be cool about that. He has asked himself why, for instance, he translated Mayakovsky into Scots and concludes that he did so partly because Scots seemed closer to the Russian's tough, slangy use of words but also because, after all, he did feel a patriotic challenge there. Morgan's second reaction to the fact of Scottishness has been, in common with most of his six brethren in this book and related exhibitions, to work feverishly against the dangers of provincialism by importing culture from the big world the other side of England. His industry as a translator is incredible. He has tried his hand with at least eight Russian poets, with the Spanish of Neruda and Lorca, the German of Hölderlin, Brecht, von Platen, Enzensberger, the Italian of Montale (a favourite), with French and Anglo-Saxon and the rendering of Shakespeare into Scots. He has translated Petöfi and Weöres from the Hungarian. Even that list is hopelessly incomplete. And as an academic intellectual, his critical work is read throughout the English-speaking world and has been one of the principal provokers of the surge of American and English interest in modern Scottish literature.

What sort of poet is he? A man who has darted so rapidly between forms and themes can't be summed up by any single work. And yet it wouldn't be too hard to guess out an unsigned Morgan. The technical ability glows. The rhetoric snaps at you ("Decided/Demons fill the cracks with smoke"). The generous, excited mind slashes open the mattress in which its savings are packed. This is the poet who wrote, in the preface to his collected essays: "CHANGE RULES is the supreme graffito"!

Note

Individual poems mentioned by Neal Ascherson can be found in the following collections, details of which are given in the individual selected bibliographies: Norman MacCaig *Old Maps and New;* Iain Crichton Smith *Selected Poems;* George Mackay Brown *Selected Poems* ('Dead Fires', 'Love Letter'), *Winterfold* ('Unpopular Fisherman,' 'Afternoon Tea'); Robert Garioch *Collected Poems;* Sorley MacLean *Spring tide and Neap tide.* See also: *Hugh MacDiarmid Complete Poems 1920-1976* Martin Brian and O'Keafe 1978; and Edwin Morgan *The Whittrick* (Akros, 1973).

Edwin Morgan (1979)
Coloured pencil on cream paper
10⅝ × 8½ inches

Six Poets
Interviewed by
Marshall Walker

Norman MacCaig
Iain Crichton Smith
George Mackay Brown
Robert Garioch
Sorley MacLean
Edwin Morgan

Left: Norman MacCaig (1968)
Oil on hardboard, 48 × 36 inches
Collection: Scottish National Portrait Gallery

Right: Norman MacCaig (1979)
Oil on canvas, 78 × 42 inches

Norman MacCaig

I'm a helpless collector, and this is called **Helpless Collector:**

Events come
bringing me presents—
more, as has been said, than the sands of the sea,
more, as has been said oftener, than the stars in the sky.

There's no refusal.
I'm the exultant possessor
of the ones that please me. I try to be
only the caretaker
of the ones I hate.

They won't let me.

I put the crooked mask
behind the delicate poem
and it moves to the front.

What sort of events please you?
Oh, boy! Will you give me till February? Opening my eyes and seeing what's in front of them. People. Oh, that's an impossible question. Millions of events please me.

What kind of events do you hate?
Death. Other people's. I've lost friends in the last six years, and I hate that. For selfish reasons, because they're dead. They don't know anything about it, but I do.

One of those deaths has led to a sequence of poems recently published in The Equal Skies . . . *a book in which you seem to be a little more personal, a little more open . . . not, perhaps, quite so much in hiding as you have been.*
I'll adjust that! . . . The amazing thing about that particular man was that he was what careerists would call an absolute failure. In fact, the people up there in Lochinver,

when he died, when I was there, said, 'Oh, you know, he could have been Manager of the Bank of England, he could have been Prime Minister,' because he was a very intelligent man. (Couldn't keep a job for three weeks!) And I thought, 'You fools, all his life he has spread more joy than anybody I've ever known.' To me, he was a total success. Of these poems this is the one that's most directly concerned with the kind of chap he was, and it's called **Praise of a Man:**

He went through a company like a lamplighter—
see the dull minds, one after another,
begin to glow, to shed
a beneficent light.

He went through a company like
a knifegrinder—see the dull minds
scattering sparks of themselves,
becoming razory, becoming useful.

He went through a company
as himself. But now he's one
of the multitudinous company of the dead
where are no individuals.

The beneficent lights dim
but don't vanish. The razory edges
dull, but still cut. He's gone: but you can see
his tracks still, in the snow of the world.

The places that seem to matter to you most are Edinburgh and Assynt, which you have described as the most seductive part of Scotland. One of the recent poems 'Me as Traveller'—*in* The Equal Skies *asserts a very strong disinclination to travel—presumably, far from these places.*

I don't know how much one is influenced by one's own invented phrases . . . Once, being urged to go abroad—you know, 'widen my horizons'—(Your horizons are inside your skull, for a start) I said, 'I'm in a plush-lined rut and don't intend to leave it.' I was never very interested in travelling away . . . I've lived in Edinburgh all my life and I love it, but I don't write about it. It's an old coat, to me, taken for granted, a Joseph's coat of many colours . . . It's curious that I don't write about it. In the same way, I've been a school-teacher all my life and I never write about children. Do you know why? . . . I hate them after half-past three! Up till then I like them fine . . . And I've found, in this corner—Assynt, Lochinver area—a landscape which is so beautiful. And it's linear. The mountains are small, but you see them from their ankles to the tops of their skulls, so they look about three times their cheating, conning height. And you only have to walk two hundred yards and you get a new view, and I'm lazy. If you are in the Cairngorms you walk four miles, but up there you just turn the corner . . . My ideal—and if somebody would give me some money it would become a fact—would be to spend the six winter months in Edinburgh and the six summer months up there. Because I need both. I love both.

You love, in particular, Ben Suilven.

Suilven, please. I'm a pedant. Yes, I love Suilven, because from the West it looks like the top joint of your thumb. But he cons you: there's a ridge and there's a pinky at the far end, so that he is infinitely variable. And he spouts cool clear water from innumerable springs . . . In my hot youth—last Thursday—I climbed one of the local hills up there, these miniature Alps, and I hurt my knee. It's awful steep. There's a narrow ridge, so that when you get on to the ridge, suddenly you see miles and miles instead of just what was under you . . . **Climbing Suilven:**

I nod and nod to my own shadow and thrust
A mountain down and down.
Between my feet a loch shines in the brown,
Its silver paper crinkled and edged with rust.
My lungs say No;
But down and down this treadmill hill must go.

Parishes dwindle. But my parish is
This stone, that tuft, this stone
And the cramped quarters of my flesh and bone.
I claw that tall horizon down to this;
And suddenly
My shadow jumps huge miles away from me.

I don't like people making mountains, or, indeed, other people, into metaphors. I hate it. I think a person is a person . . . and I don't like burdening other people with your own fascinating interests. The same with mountains. In **No Accident** I make a metaphor of it. I climbed Suilven; I hurt a cartilage; I had a terrible walk—and it's a metaphor.

Walking downhill from Suilven (a fine day, for once)
I twisted a knee. Two crippling miles to walk.
Leap became lower. Bag swung from a bowed neck.
Pedant of walking learned it like a dunce.

I didn't mind so much. Suilven's a place
That gives more than a basket of trout. It opens
The space it lives in and a heaven's revealed, in glimpses.
Grace is a crippling thing. You've to pay for grace.

The heaven's an odd one, shaped like cliff and scree
No less than they are: no picnicking place, but hiding
Forevers and everywheres in every thing—including
A two-mile walk, even, and a crippled knee.

You reach it by revelation. Good works can't place
Heaven in a dead hind and a falcon going
Or on the hard truth that, if only by being
First in a lower state, you've to pay for grace.

The poem ends with the observation, 'you've to pay for grace'. The suggestion, perhaps, is that you are even prepared to pay for grace yourself?
Not me.

You are not a transcendentalist at all?
Absolutely not. I don't believe in grace for a start. I believe in good works, but not grace. I don't believe in God, but I believe in the Devil. I'm a Zen Calvinist.

In one of the poems to Angus MacLeod you talk about the minister spreading a 'pollution of bad beliefs'. Those would have included belief in the Devil, presumably, in that part of the country.
I don't believe in the Devil. I just got ridiculous for a moment. No, I don't want to talk about this because I hate that kind of religious belief very desperately, and I don't want to hurt people whom I like by saying what I think about their obscene beliefs, which seem to me to be not religious at all, but only theological. And theology has the same relation to religion as criticism has to literature . . .

Hugh MacDiarmid almost forgave you for writing in English. He certainly admired you greatly.
No, he didn't. He liked me. He didn't admire me at all. I liked him, and I didn't admire him at all.

But he did like your work.
No, he didn't.

Well, he said he did. Think he was lying in his teeth?
My teeth.

When he was lying in your teeth, he said that one of the things he admired most was the elegance of wit in your poems. This is an aspect of your work that has been talked about a great deal. Adverse criticism has accused you of elevating wit above all else, and I wonder how you've reacted to that . . .
Oh, it hurts and cripples me! I crawl into a corner; I bedew my midnight pillow with tears, until I think of Bach and Mozart, who did exactly the same thing—sometimes! I know the danger of this, of course—my danger. The danger is that you get flippant, and when wit, to call it by that dubious word, degenerates into flippancy—oh, well, that's silly. And I do that—I know I do it . . . I think, maybe, it's defensive, like irony.

Do you think, perhaps, there's a recoil in people from sheer precision?
Oh, yes. They don't like people who are cleverer than they are . . . When it comes to this sort of wit stuff, I think I am quite good at it, and chaps that don't have it resent it, you know . . . I am not at all sure about this. I know that it's a thing I have to watch when I am writing, because I can be seduced by what you friendlily call wit, which at its worst is

flippancy. But I can't help it. That's the way my mind works . . . Listen: I am not telling people about me. When I write a poem, when a man is painting a picture, composing a piece of music, he is not concerned in telling other people about him. He actually does it, but that is not his intention. And when I write a poem I am just trying to make a little sequence of 'verbojuices' which would, I hope, stand in their own glass, so that somebody can pick it up . . . Oh, metaphor, you see . . .! I'm always jumping into metaphor, doing a failed sidestroke to the back.

You are very aware of your own act of perception, aren't you?
No.

Well, take for example the poem 'An Ordinary Day' *(Old Maps and New) which begins 'I took my mind a walk, or my mind took me a walk'*
O.K. You win.

You write a lot about animals.
I pat earwigs on the head and I call slaters by their first name.

You might almost be said to be a frog fetishist.
I'm glad you said 'almost'. I like frogs.

A recent poem about a toad seems a good example of a kind of poem you often write. It's comical, but if readers assume that it's just comical, you surprise them.
. . . This is one of the toads I was familiar with. Don't 'phone 'The News of the World', boy! He used to wriggle under an imperceptible door and sit in the lobby. **Toad:**

Stop looking like a purse. How could a purse
squeeze under the rickety door and sit,
full of satisfaction, in a man's house?

You clamber towards me on your four corners—
one hand, one foot, one hand, one foot.

I love you for being a toad,
for crawling like a Japanese wrestler,
and for not being frightened.

I put you in my purse hand, not shutting it,
and set you down outside directly under
every star.

A jewel in your head? Toad,
you've put one in mine,
a tiny radiance in a dark place.

You go into a dark place with another poem, this time about a snake. What was the attraction of the snake here?
I suppose, basically, my detestation of religion and, of course, what's happened in history and in my lifetime. The villains making excuses, you know.

You feel your way into the snake as a way, then, of using the snake to say something bigger than the poem at first appears . . .
Oh, I think that kind of talk stinks the joint up, as Ellington said when they asked him if he was influenced by Debussy. I don't know about the process of writing a poem at all. I recollect the poem you are talking about, and I suppose it's about the excuses people make for their evil blunders, if not intentions—'Wisnae me, came from a broken home'—all that stuff. 'I had a black-out'—this, after sawing a woman in quadruplets. I don't like that sort of thing. I think you are responsible for what you think and, particularly, for what you do.

The poem is really about the way men abrogate their responsibilities by projecting them on to something else.
Yes . . . This poem is called **The First of Them**—the excusers.

The snake weeps below the tree.
He has been hated for so long.

Even Adam and Eve were no sooner past
that fiery sword than they began
to abuse him.

And the things that have been said about him
ever since—by parents to children,
by priests and lawmakers.

Poor snake. He crawls on his belly
dropping amber tears in the dust and whining
I was only obeying orders.

You have a recent poem called 'Equilibrist' *which seems as close to a self-portrait of you as you are now as one could hope to get.*
I suppose it doesn't give away much, but I suppose it is—oh, I hate the word—confessional . . . It's an appeal to my friends to like me.

Why is the appeal necessary?
Because I like my friends and I would like to be liked by them. I think people are far more important than poetry . . . In the last book—many people have noticed this—this cold, valuable fish has started to admit that he suffers, and the reason to me is quite clear. In the last five years I have lost six of my closest friends and it has become—I hate the way I am going to say this—possible for me as a writer to talk about it. I'm a publicly suffering man in a way that I wasn't until five or six years ago . . . **Equilibrist:**

I see an adder and, a yard away,
a butterfly being gorgeous. I switch the radio
from tortures in foreign prisons
to a sonata of Schubert (that foreigner).
I crawl from the swamp of nightmare into
a glittering rainfall, a swathing of sunlight.

Noticing you can do nothing about.
It's the balancing that shakes my mind.

What my friends don't notice
is the weight of joy in my right hand
and the weight of sadness in my left.
All they see is MacCaig being upright,
easy-oasy and jocose.

I had a difficulty in being friendly
to the Lord, who gave us these burdens,
so I returned him to other people
and totter without help
among his careless inventions.

As everybody knows, I am a very pure, innocent person, but I know damn well there are things in me which are very awful, and this, I suppose, is about them. **Go Away, Ariel:**

Heartless, musical Ariel,
does everyone prefer Caliban to you,
as I do?

Supersonic Ariel, go zip round the world
or curl up in a cowslip's bell.
I'd rather be visited by Caliban.

—As I am, I am. I chat with him
helplessly spilling out of an armchair,
scaly on the carpet.

I'm teaching him to smoke. It soothes him
when he blubbers about Miranda and
goes on about his mother.

Phone a bat, Ariel. Leave us
to have a good cry—to stare at each other
with recognition and loathing.

Are you very conscious of MacDiarmid as an influence or a presence?
A presence, but not an influence . . . Oh, he has to be . . . I was a very close friend of Chris's and I disagreed with practically every thing he said—which means I agreed with practically everything he said, because everything he said had two faces . . . He must have altered the convolutions in my brain . . . but he didn't influence me as a writer, because his wild desires and powerful intentions weren't the same as mine at all . . . As a writer, as a writer—as if you could distinguish the writer from the man! Oh. I have such relishing recollections . . . I've grown not to be frightened of the word 'love'. I loved him and he loved me .

Did he influence you in any particular love of your country?
No, I don't think so, and the reason to me is plain and obvious: he didn't know what Scotland was . . . It was an idea, a concept in his brain, which it is to most Scots.

Is it not so in your brain?
No..

How Scottish are you?
Hundred per cent. Infuriated with distilled water. I don't like the Scots, and I don't like their history. Liars, murderers, traitors, not only in the Highlands, the Borders as well. I think the Scots are awful. I think the Portuguese are awful. I think the Sicilians are awful. I think everybody's awful, except when you meet a particular instance, and some of them are so wonderful and marvellous . . . and don't tell me they came from their filthy history.

Edinburgh, 28th September 1980

Norman MacCaig (1979)
Coloured pencil on grey paper
19¾ × 12¾ inches

Leaders of Men

Flourishing signatures and smiles,
they gather round the conference table.

In each heart the devil sits crosslegged,
grinning and cracking his finger joints.

And outside the door the last angel
huddles its rags about it and weeps
from bruised eyes. It has the same name
everywhere in the world.

It weeps,
helplessly hearing the cry
of the helpless, the tortured, the bereaved
calling and calling
in all the languages of the world.

Rewards and Furies

In a ship hardly bigger than this room,
with a mind narrower than this pen,
with a library of one book
and that book with one word in it,
Columbus sailed and sailed and arrived.

The poor soul didn't know where.

Still, he succeeded:
Indians were massacred, railways
opened up wheatfields, jails and asylums,
and skyscrapers walked around
with atom bombs slung at their hips.

I hope Columbus didn't believe
in his own ghost. How could it rest
through these hundreds of years?
How could it stare into the future
at his monstrous descendants
ignorantly sailing, ignorantly arriving?

Christmas Tree

Take the star off it.
It's shed its ghastly light
for two thousand years too many.

Cut the string of those glass baubles,
blue as death, orange as rage—
and the ones filled
with green acid. Let them
smash on the floor.

Cram the little presents
in your heart, where they belong.

Then throw the tree
on the trash heap. What use is it
stripped of its lies?

The sad thing is there's a tree
you can't cut down. It grows
inside you.

Sometimes,
when you're taken off your guard,
I think I see
the blasphemous fairylights
and the dreadful angel on top
looking out of your eyes.

19th Floor Nightmare, New York

The party had been a drunken one
so she sleeps a deep sleep
on the 19th floor
of the Mandragora Hotel.

And she dreams, she dreams
of bodiless horrors
and horrible bodies.
Her car crashes over a bridge
and her pillow's on fire.
But when a fur-gloved hand
lands on her face, she wakes
at the end of a scream.
Lordy, Lordy, she says,
Just a dream, just a nightmare.

Trembling, she gets up
and goes to the window.
Trembling, she pulls open the curtain
and looks out, straight
into the left eye of King Kong.

Norman MacCaig
Edinburgh, 1980
Photographer: Jessie Ann Matthew

Norman Alexander MacCaig

Norman MacCaig was born in Edinburgh on 14th November 1910. He was educated at the Royal High School, where he began writing poems, and Edinburgh University, graduating MA with Honours in Classics in 1932. He worked as a schoolmaster 1934-1967, and as headmaster 1969-70. From 1967 to 1969 he was Fellow in Creative Writing at Edinburgh University; 1970-72 Lecturer in English Studies and from 1972 Reader in Poetry at Stirling University.

Awards: SAC awards 1954, 1966, 1970, 1971, 1978; Society of Authors grant, 1964, prize, 1967; Heinemann Award 1967; F.R.S.L. 1965; O.B.E. 1979.

In the late 1930s and early '40s MacCaig was associated, as were other Scots poets, Tom Scott, J. F. Hendry, G. S. Fraser, with the New Apocalypse movement: a heady mixture of influences, Surrealism, Dylan Thomas, and Herbert Read among them. The movement was short-lived and its members developed in different directions: from "lunging and plunging on images" (M. Lindsay) MacCaig since then has been on what he describes as "the long haul towards lucidity". The materials for his poems are "ideas, feelings, people and landscapes—particularly the astonishing assembly of shapes that make up Edinburgh . . . and the (to me) most seductive part of Scotland, that lies in the North-West, around the village of Lochinver. But of course one is influenced by, simply, everything. For the senses, the 'five ports of knowledge', are so hospitable to everything, and into them sail, with luck, the most remarkable cargoes." (Norman MacCaig in *Worlds,* p.162).

"Art . . . is concerned with form, and that's to say, with order. I don't know whether artists see an order in the chaos of experience that other people don't or whether they impose an order on that chaos. But that order must be there." (from "My Way of It," originally published in *Chapman* magazine and reprinted in *As I Remember).*

Selected Publications

Poetry: *Far Cry: poems* (Routledge 1943); *The Inward Eye* (Routledge 1946); *Riding Lights* (Hogarth 1955); *A Common Grace* (Chatto & Windus/Hogarth 1960); *Rings on a Tree* (Chatto/Hogarth 1968); *A Man in My Position* (Chatto/Hogarth 1969); *Selected Poems* (Hogarth 1971); *The World's Room* (Chatto/Hogarth 1974); *Tree of Strings* (Hogarth 1977); *Old Maps and New: selected poems* (Hogarth 1978); *The Equal Skies* (Chatto/Hogarth 1980)

Anthologies: *Twelve Modern Scottish Poets,* ed. C. King (University of London Press 1971); *Penguin Modern Poets* 21 (1972—with I. C. Smith & G. M. Brown); *Modern Scottish Poetry* ed. M. Lindsay (Carcanet 1976)

Recording: *The Way I Say It* (Claddagh Records 1971)

Edited: *Honour'd Shade: an anthology of new Scottish poetry* (Chambers 1959); *Contemporary Scottish Verse 1959-1969* (Calder 1970—with Alex Scott)

Critical Studies: R. Fulton, *Contemporary Scottish Poetry* (Macdonald 1974), pp. 69-87; W. S. Porter, "The Poetry of Norman MacCaig", *Akros* 32, December 1976; E. Frykman, *Unemphatic Marvels: a study of Norman MacCaig's poetry* (Göteborg: Acta Universitatis Gothoburgensis 1977)

See also: N. MacCaig, "My Way of It", *As I Remember: ten Scottish authors recall how writing began for them,* ed. M. Lindsay (Hale 1979); *Worlds: seven modern poets,* ed. G. Summerfield (Penguin 1974), pp.161-84; *Akros* 7, March 1968 (MacCaig issue)

Iain Crichton Smith (1980)
Oil on canvas, 36 × 60 inches

Iain Crichton Smith

We have been looking at Alexander Moffat's portrait of you . . . but you have gone in for a little self-depiction recently in a new poem called **Self-portrait** *. . . Could we begin our discussion with that?*

Whose is this Free Church face?
Surely it's someone else, from my childhood,
making its endless principled demands
through the round glasses' twin gun-barrels.
There was a time I would have mocked you, face,
in your gaunt heaven fixed, so smug and clear,
now I bear you with me like a penance.
Remember those stones, those thorns, those bleak winds,
those cottages ringed so constantly by daisies.
Surely they made you, those secret moral waters,
in the night when you were not looking, in the day.

You start off talking about your 'Free Church face', and that at least tells us that you have some connection, however oblique, with religion. You call your glasses 'gun-barrels', so you do gun things down, you are a satirist. You refer powerfully if briefly to your background—the background of a place—and you talk about a secret moral force which is other than the force of the Church. You've got all this into a very short poem, which I think is a remarkable achievement in itself. Would you say something about the importance of your religion, the 'Free Church face' part of your portrait?

Well, as you know, I grew up on the island of Lewis, which is a strongly religious island, and sometimes I feel that there are Free Church or religious elements in me which are in conflict with my art. I feel this conflict a great deal. To grow up in an island like Lewis is, obviously, to be, in a sense, constricted as far as art is concerned. Now, my attitude to Free Church and religion is very ambivalent. You see, in one sense I think of it as constricting, and, in another sense, I admire the people who belong to that church because they represent, in a very strong and almost unquestioning way, things which I find very difficult and very complex. One of the things I have had to find out as a poet is how to release the complexities within myself, not to find simple answers, because I think it is easy, coming from an island where religion is so strong, to think that you can find simple spiritual answers. So, religion is very important to me as a kind of force that I react against.

Could we compare two different yet in some ways kindred reactions in two of your poems. They both illustrate your response to what you call 'the churches' declaiming'. The first poem is 'Old Woman' *from your* Selected Poems.

This actually was written in Lewis. I was up on holiday and went into this house in the village where I was staying at the time. There was this old woman lying in a bed. Her husband was a Free Church elder. She was so old and weak he had to help her to eat. He put the plate in front of her and spooned the stuff into her mouth. I remember coming out of the house and thinking of the contrast between the degradation in the house and the beautiful summer's day outside. It made a tremendous impact on me, this kind of helplessness, utter helplessness. **Old Woman:**

And she, being old, fed from a mashed plate
as an old mare might droop across a fence
to the dull pastures of its ignorance.
Her husband held her upright while he prayed

to God who is all-forgiving to send down
some angel somewhere who might land perhaps
in his foreign wings among the gradual crops.
She munched, half dead, blindly searching the spoon.

Outside, the grass was raging. There I sat
imprisoned in my pity and my shame
that men and women having suffered time
should sit in such a place, in such a state

and wished to be away, yes, to be far away
with athletes, heroes, Greeks or Roman men
who pushed their bitter spears into a vein
and would not spend an hour with such decay.

"Pray God," he said, "we ask you, God," he said.
The bowed back was quiet. I saw the teeth
tighten their grip around a delicate death.
And nothing moved within the knotted head

but only a few poor veins as one might see
vague wishless seaweed floating on a tide
of all the salty waters where had died
too many waves to mark two more or three.

I suppose what happened in that second part—that image of the seaweed and the veins in the head—was that after I left the house, I went down to the shore and looked from a headland on to the water below. I saw the seaweed swishing about the tide, and there seemed to be a connection between the seaweed and the sort of veins that stood out on the woman's forehead . . . Whenever I am talking about creativity, I always talk about these kinds of connections which you get when you are writing, maybe, at your best, or when you are writing very creatively.

Yet the force of the poem remains dependent on the earlier imagery. Outside the house 'the grass was raging', and, despite whatever consolation there may be towards the end, you are . . . raging, too. I'd like to set against that poem a very short one from The Permanent Island, *the collection originally published in Gaelic which you translated yourself. This is called* 'The Old Woman'. *We're told, 'The postman will come tonight with the Christmas letter ', and the poem asks, 'Does anyone know what will be in the letter?' The answer is, 'The sharp star of the Bible'. Does this illustrate the ambivalence you were talking about? It is the consoling 'star' of the Bible, but it is also 'sharp', it cuts. Is this the kind of effect you had in mind?*
Yes. My mother was very Free Church and very often the poems that I write about old women are, in effect, dealing with the kind of people that my mother was. I used to find that, though I myself felt there was little consolation in the Bible, for them there was. They had a tremendous certainty. I am quite sure that my mother, for instance, thought that when she died it wouldn't be the end in a way that I wouldn't think. So this is part of the ambivalence that I feel—the certainty that some people have, the certainty that I would like to have, but don't have because I feel more of the complex than they do . . .

Do you think your sense of the complex precludes you for ever from what they had?
Yes, I think so. There's a poem called *Lenin* in which I say something like this. Lenin for me is someone with a simplicity of mind, you know, the central certainty. **Lenin:**

In a chair of iron
sits coldly my image of Lenin,
that troubling man
"who never read a book for pleasure."

The germ inside the sealed train
emerged, spread in wind and rain
into new minds in revolution
seeming more real than had been,

for instance, Dostoevsky. No, I can
romanticise no more that "head of iron,"
"the thought and will unalterably one,"
"the word-doer," "thunderer," "the stone

rolling through clouds." Simple to condemn
the unsymmetrical, simple to condone
that which oneself is not. By admiration
purge one's envy of unadult iron

when the true dialectic is to turn
in the infinitely complex, like a chain
we steadily burn through, steadily forge and burn
not to be dismissed in any poem

by admiration for the ruthless man
nor for the saint but for the moving on
into the endlessly various, real, human,
world which is no new era, shining dawn.

The point is that I am looking for the infinitely complex. I see Lenin as someone who belongs to a kind of religion . . . I suppose communism is a kind of religion with the singleness that I was talking about . . . Lenin, though an admirable man in some ways, is a kind of man I would never like to be, because I would prefer to be someone like Dostoevsky, who sees the infinitely complex.

'The infinitely complex' takes us, perhaps, to another poem in Selected Poems *where many strands of feeling weave together to make a total effect which, I think, does puzzle some readers—***Sunday Morning Walk:**

Sunday of wrangling bells—and salt in the air—
I passed the tall black men and their women walking
over the tight-locked streets which were all on fire
with summer ascendant. The seas were talking and talking

as I took my way to the wood where the river ran quiet.
The grass lay windowed in sunlight, the leaves were raging
in furious dying green. The road turned right
round the upstanding castle whose stone, unaging,

marks how a world remains as I, being now
pack of a wandering flesh, take holiday, strolling
far from the churches' declaiming. Health will allow
riots of naiads and nymphs, so wantonly rolling

with me in leaves in woods, thinking how once
Jove took his pleasure of Leda or—splendid embracing—
god would mate with a goddess—rapid the pounce,
fruitful the hot-thighed meeting, no need for unlacing.

And occupied thus, I came where a dead sheep lay
close to a fence, days gone. The flies were hissing and buzzing
out of the boiling eyes, wide open as day.
I stood in the sunlight beside it, watching and musing.

Three crows famished yards off. Live sheep grazed far
from the rotting carcass. The jaw, well-shaved, lay slackly
there on the warm quiet grass. The household air
was busy with buzzing like fever. How quickly, how quickly

the wool was peeled from the back! How still was the flesh!
How the visiting flies would not knock at the door of the sockets!
How the hole in the side gaped red, a well-sized gash!
How the clear young lambs grazed in the shade of the thickets!

And the sun blazed hot on my shoulder. Here was no shade.
But the sheep was quiet, so quiet. There was nothing to notice
but the grape-bunched flies and the crows. Could a world have stayed
if I'd taken a stick in my hand to beat off the flies?

They would merely return when I'd gone and busy as always
inhabit this larder again no matter how brightly
I struck with my smart sharp stick. All I could praise—
yes, all I could praise—was the sheep lying there so quietly

not knowing, not knowing. High summer was raging around.
I stood in my slack clean clothes. The stones were burning.
The flies in the wound continued their occupied sound
as I turned my back on a death of no weeping or mourning.

I wrote this when I was up in Lewis on holiday. I was at the castle just outside Stornoway, and I saw this dead sheep. I think what I am trying to say in this poem is that the sheep felt nothing when it died. In writing it, I thought of that poem by Yeats where he says that man has created death . . . and that the best thing would be if one could die without any conception of religion or anything like that. Just to feel that you are simply dead and that is the end of it.

Death is something you're very interested in, isn't it? You have actually said that everything you've done eventually comes to the question of what death is: 'What is a dead person, and in the end what is the value of writing when one is confronted by a dead person?' The opening poems

of Selected Poems *are all concerned in some way with death. Why is this such a dominant interest?*
I suppose being a Highlander . . . When I was growing up in Lewis, between the wars mostly, I found that a lot of people living on the island were old people and that I was one of the few young people in the village . . . When my mother died, I went up and looked at her face in the coffin, and I felt that the face, the whole body were absolutely wooden . . . I felt that this was nothing to do with me at all, that death . . . was beyond any kind of thing that we could think about, that we couldn't think about it at all. I know, coming from Oban, coming from Lewis, I shouldn't be talking about someone like Wittgenstein, but he says that death is not a fact of life. It was only then that I realised that death is something other . . . you know, its strangeness . . . and in the Highlands one is surrounded by a kind of dying in the language, in the aged people . . .

Lewis and Oban, where you live now, are both very important to you, yet you are able to feel very concernedly for things that lie far beyond them. In the Gaelic poem which you translate in The Permanent Island *as* 'Going Home' *you talk about going home to your island . . . but you also say 'I will be thinking about the great fire that is behind our thoughts', and this is the fire of Nagasaki and Hiroshima. Your volume,* From Bourgeois Land *is full of this sort of thing . . . What is the connection between Oban or Lewis and this sense of the world beyond, the Nagasakis, Hiroshimas or Vietnams?*
Living on an island is a very strange thing. You lead a very sheltered life. In Lewis, for instance, the newspapers don't come in until maybe the following day—at least when I was growing up . . . To go home to an island, to leave an island is a very traumatic experience for the kind of people we are . . . In the village where I grew up, roughly between 1939 and 1945, I used to think of all the islands. There were many islands which had been attacked, like Crete, Malta. I used to think, well, we're all vulnerable, we are able to be attacked from outside. I think this led me to these kinds of ideas about Vietnam, Nagasaki, Hiroshima. No matter where you live, whether you think it's beautiful or whatever, nevertheless it's vulnerable.

I'll tell you a story . . . When I was little, in the island of Lewis, I'd never seen a theatre in my whole life . . . I went to university at the age of seventeen. I arrived at Aberdeen Railway Station, having travelled from Lewis, and I saw a beggar. He was wearing black glasses and there was a cap beside him with pennies in it. He was looking for me, or whoever was coming out of the Station, to give him some money. I thought, 'This is impossible. You can't have this.' On the island of Lewis you could never have beggars. In the village where I grew up, if there was someone who was poor, he or she would be looked after, and I thought there was something extraordinary about this, that someone could so openly, so publicly admit to being so vulnerable, to put a cap on the pavement and look for pennies.

Ever since then I think that I have this feeling for vulnerable people. Maybe because I come from a close community I see it more clearly than I would otherwise. You know that there are people in the world who are dependent on others in a way that, in a community like Lewis, you would never be dependent. For instance, if you were on Lewis, and , say, you had peats to be gathered and you were an old woman, all the people in the village would come, and for that whole day they would bring in the peats . . . It was a closely knit community, and you could walk into anybody's house at any time . . . You didn't need to knock, you just walked in . . . It was an organism, a complete . . . living organism . . . if you twitched one part of the village organism, the rest of the organism twitched. So the feeling I had, once I left the island, was that I realised for the first time that there are people who need things, who didn't have this kind of community.

Community is very important to me. I feel privileged in a way . . . when I see pictures on television about Uganda and such places: they are terrifying. You know that, these people . . . there's no one to look after them, whereas, in the village where I lived, if you were ill, someone would always be there to look after you.

Scotland is very important to you, but you've said, 'I very often feel ashamed of Scotland'. Why?
At the time I wrote that I felt there were only two important

things in Scotland: Celtic Football Club and Hugh MacDiarmid . . . Celtic had just won the European Cup . . . I've often felt about Scotland, there's a kind of mediocrity that you see in their football. At a certain stage they say, 'We're going to win the World Cup,' but they don't. There's a lack of professionalism, which I feel is very important . . . It is very important to me in poetry that I should be professional in my attitude—as I think MacDiarmid was and Celtic Football Club was. There was a period when I was writing my poetry when I felt—and possibly MacDiarmid felt the same—a kind of blackness . . . that you are shouting into a room which echoes back to you . . . It's a hollow echo, there's nothing there . . .

. . .there's no audience?
Well, no, not just that there's no audience. There are no ideas, nothing that can allow you to write poetry. Compare, for instance, what's happening in Ireland. I think the Irish poets are very lucky, in a sense, because they have to deal with real things. I sometimes feel there is nothing real in Scotland that you can actually operate on to make real poetry . . . there's nothing going on . . .

But surely there's been a great deal going on, politically . . . even if much of it has been frustrating. Poetically, in literature there's a great deal going on. Surely this is an extremely vital time in Scotland?
Well, to go back to Hugh MacDiarmid again, he says that the Scottish poet must assume the burden of his people's doom, and he also says the Scottish people can never learn . . . You have this feeling that there is nothing new going on, that what is going on is basically superficial. Take the Referendum . . . I remember the day . . . and I must admit that I am not a Scottish Nationalist . . . on that particular day I thought, 'Is it possible to commit yourself to the new, to make a leap into the new?' And I felt—I feel all the time that there isn't enough of this leap. It's just talking about what has gone on in the past.

Oban, 21st September 1980

Islander

Ash on an old man's sleeve—
you sit in your bare kitchen
brow furrowed at your table
and the words of your muttered grace
are quite unintelligible,
you in this humble corner
not affording God's roses
but thorns only and cabbages:
while through the window I see
the alien oil-rig planted
deep in this friendly water.

Like poetry its pipes bring up
the oil from the sea's depths:
it travels from hope to hope.

But you sit gravely here
having travelled America,
fixed in your limiting place,
in your blue dungarees,
staring down at your garden,
its turnips and cabbages,
the winding roots of potatoes,
clutching known darknesses,

and your shifting canvas jacket
sailing the local air.

Childhood and Adulthood

The window opened. Two small boys were playing.
"Is the gnome hiding? Is it really hiding?"
They pushed their heads inside the well of leaves.

Running we were, the rim of the sky came up
suddenly like a fence cutting our faces.
We stopped, dazed, in the discolouring light.

The woman threw buckets of water on the thorns.

The gnome bounced back and forward. "What does it say?
Tell me, tell me." The trees were a green sway.
There is no garden privater than this.

We were hauled back, though birds flew in the air.
The small blond heads are tight, crammed with our loss.
They stare at us with such brightness we turn away.

Near Oban

Morning and the sea calm
with trees growing upside down
in brine greenly. A fawn
strides into the high wood
prick-eared, long-legged, the sun
reddening its brown skin.
Freely it strides up. We stare
from our parked car. Everywhere
silence, and the trembling dew
in clear chains. We drive on,
not speaking, into Oban
and to our work, the offices
with the tight covers still on
the typewriters, and the phone
quiet in its black cradle.

Accident Prone

If it's not his leg that limps, then his face is cut.
He arrives at night with blood about his eyes
and shaping red roses on his torn shirt.
Accidents look for him to happen to.

O world are you not like this, limping and gory?
And do you not, like him, trust to the same arms—
pretending that your accidents are glory—
for if not that what else can we call them by?

The Ghost

Dead, she swam towards me in the light.
"I have seen you before," I said.
"I have sat on a bench beside you by the sea."
Her tiny bones were like the tenderest flutes.
She smiled and smiled. I couldn't tell if it was
forgiveness or a waiting or a threat.
If there's a heaven it wasn't where those seats were.
If there's a hell it's the absence, the return.

Iain Crichton Smith (1980)
Pastel on coloured paper, 15¼ × 20½ inches

Problem

We listen to your story of the bully.
How shall we help you? For if we say we'll do
there is the unalterable law of not grassing.
There is also equally the unalterable law
that things will only grow worse because of our aid.

Shall the nations remain helpless in the mornings
of pity but no interference? Shall the child
hold out its hand eternally for mercy?
All we can say is, when you grow old
you will meet the same bully over and over

in mirror after mirror. Is our advice, then,
O learn to hide, O keep a low profile,
smile at the wounding speech, O learn to smile.
Or, if not that, lash out in helpless fury,
stand up for what we made you, in that duel.

Wearing your helpless glasses, you ask a question.
The answer is, there's no answer but your own.
The solutions have all been tried. We have come through
but at what a cost, faces flattened by pain,
twisted by shame, equally helpless, lying.

Iain Crichton Smith
Oban, 1980
Photographer: Jessie Ann Matthew

Iain Crichton Smith
(Iain Mac a' Ghobhainn)

Iain Crichton Smith was born in the Island of Lewis on New Year's Day 1928. He was educated at the Nicholson Institute, Stornoway, and at Aberdeen University, where he graduated MA with Honours in English in 1949. Like George Mackay Brown he discovered a talent for writing essays at school; and again like Brown his youth was beset by illness, in Smith's case bronchitis and asthma, and the enforced leisure gave him time to read. He was a sergeant in the British Army Education Corps 1950-52. He taught English at Clydebank for three years before going back north, to Oban, where he taught from 1955 to 1977. Since then he has been a freelance writer and recently has been engaged in translating Gaelic poetry from the sixteenth to the twentieth century into English. In 1980 he was Visiting Fellow at Canberra University. He is a prolific writer, being playwright, novelist, writer of short stories, translator (of among other Gaelic works, Sorley MacLean's *Dàin do Eimhir),* and critic as well as poet. He is bilingual in Gaelic and English.

Awards: Eight Scottish Arts Council awards; Book Council award 1970; Silver Pen award 1971; Poetry Book Society Recommendation 1972, 1975; awards for Gaelic plays and for Gaelic short stories; Lewis and Harris Cup 1979; F.R.S.L.; O.B.E. 1980.

In a radio talk on his poetry he commented: "I have always believed in a poetry which contains fighting tensions and not in a poetry of statement". One of the tensions he has indicated is "the conflict between discipline and freedom"—as some titles of his books show: *The Law and the Grace* and *Love Songs of a Puritan.* He admits to "no particular sources, except that I admire Lowell's work." Oban, Lewis, and the Highlands, people and place, form the subject matter of many of his poems, although he says, "I have never been interested in nature for its own sake. This may well be because I was brought up in close hard contact with it." Discussing his background he wrote that Lewis "has made me, I think, unhealthily concerned with religion so that I find I do not wholly believe in poems of the moment, but rather in poems morally shaped. I find it difficult to be humorous and joyful in my work." (*As I Remember*). However, on the positive side, as Edwin Morgan has pointed out, there is "his fascination with ideas of exactness, harmony, order, music, pattern, grace".

Selected Publications

Poetry: at least 20 volumes in Gaelic and English, including *The Long River* (Macdonald 1955); *Biobuill is Sanasan Reice* (Gairm 1965); *From Bourgeois Land* (Gollancz 1969); *Selected Poems* (Gollancz 1970); *Love Poems and Elegies* (Gollancz 1972); *The Notebooks of Robinson Crusoe* (Gollancz 1975); *The Permanent Island* (Macdonald 1975); *In the Middle* (Gollancz 1977); *River, River* (Macdonald 1978—for children)
Penguin Modern Poets 21 (1972—with G. M. Brown and N. MacCaig)

Novels: 5 volumes, including: *Consider the Lilies* (Gollancz 1968); *An End to Autumn* (Gollancz 1978)

Short stories: at least 8 volumes in Gaelic and English, including: *Burn is Aran* (Gairm 1960); *The Black and the Red* (Gollancz 1973); *The Hermit and Other Stories* (Gollancz 1977); *On the Island* (Gollancz 1979)

Criticism: *The Golden Lyric* (Akros 1967)

Interview: *Scottish International* September 1971

Critical studies: E. Morgan, "The raging and the grace: some notes on the poetry of Iain Crichton Smith," *Essays* (1974); F. Lindsay, "Disputed angels: the poetry of Iain Crichton Smith," *Akros* 36, December 1977

See also: I. C. Smith, "Between sea and moor " in *As I Remember* (Hale 1979); *Lines Review* 29, June 1969 (I.C.S. issue—includes bibliography)

George Mackay Brown (1980)
Pastel on coloured paper
11½ × 9½ inches

George Mackay Brown

You have said that without the symbolic figure of the Orkney crofter with his boat you couldn't have written any work of significance. Why do you think this is so?
These are the only people I know, really.

What else makes Orkney so important to you?
Well, I don't know. I was born here . . . It's the place I know best . . . and that's why it's important to me, I suppose. But . . . there's a union of land and sea. The fishermen and the farmers. In fact, if you go far enough back, the farmers had a boat and they got a lot of their livelihood out of the sea. I found that combination very stimulating, somehow.

Are there especially important parts of Orkney for you?
Yes, some places I like better . . . Stromness, obviously, because I live here . . . the wonderful atmosphere of Birsay . . .

The visitor to Orkney must always be struck by so many places that are full of the past.
Absolutely, because it goes so far back, of course. Far further than the Vikings, to the Picts and the broch-builders who came before them, and the neolithic people who put up the standing stones, and Maes Howe, and Skara Brae, the village on the west coast. In fact, it must have been continuously populated for over six thousand years or so.

Do you have a strong sense of continuity?
Oh, yes. Very much so.

Do you think other Orcadians have that sense?
I think they . . . breathe it in from the time they're young. Just can't avoid it.

Stromness, where you live, is the subject of the poem, **Hamnavoe,** *isn't it?*
Hamnavoe is the old name for Stromness. But in the poem it's as it was, or as I imagine it to have been, in my father's time, about the turn of the century or maybe slightly earlier:

My father passed with his penny letters
Through closes opening and shutting like legends
    When barbarous with gulls
    Hamnavoe's morning broke

On the salt and tar steps. Herring boats,
Puffing red sails, the tillers
    Of cold horizons, leaned
    Down the gull-gaunt tide

And threw dark nets on sudden silver harvests.
A stallion at the sweet fountain
    Dredged water, and touched
    Fire from steel-kissed cobbles.

Hard on noon four bearded merchants
Past the pipe-spitting pier-head strolled,
    Holy with greed, chanting
    Their slow grave jargon.

A tinker keened like a tartan gull
At cuithe-hung doors. A crofter lass
    Trudged through the lavish dung
    In a dream of cornstalks and milk.

In "The Arctic Whaler" three blue elbows fell,
Regular as waves, from beards spumy with porter,
    Till the amber day ebbed out
    To its black dregs.

The boats drove furrows homeward, like ploughmen
In blizzards of gulls. Gaelic fisher girls
    Flashed knife and dirge
    Over drifts of herring.

And boys with penny wands lured gleams
From the tangled veins of the flood. Houses went blind
    Up one steep close, for a
    Grief by the shrouded nets.

The kirk, in a gale of psalms, went heaving through
A tumult of roofs, freighted for heaven. And lovers
Unblessed by steeples, lay under
The buttered bannock of the moon.

He quenched his lantern, leaving the last door.
Because of his gay poverty that kept
My seapink innocence
From the worm and black wind;

And because, under equality's sun,
All things wear now to a common soiling,
In the fire of images
Gladly I put my hand
To save that day for him.

The character of the ferryman in Greenvoe, *Ivan Westray, suffers from 'morbus orcadensis'. What is this strange affliction?*
It's a kind of melancholy, I think, induced by the long winters and the winds that howl nearly every day here, or seem to. Not everybody has it, but I feel it in myself sometimes, a touch of this melancholy depression.

Do you think Orkney is a place where the people are especially conscious of death?
I don't think so

There is a fair bit of death in your own writing.
Yes, there is . . . **A Winter Bride:**

The three fishermen said to Jess of The Shore
'A wave took Jock
Between the Kist and The Sneuk.
We couldn't get him, however we placed the boat.
With all that drag and clutch and swell
He has maybe one in a hundred chances.'
They left some mouthing cuithes in the door.
She had stood in this threshold, fire and innocence,
A winter bride.
Now she laid off her workaday shawl,
She put on the black.

(Girl and widow across a drowned wife
Laid wondering neck on neck.)
She took the soundless choir of fish
And a sharp knife
And went the hundred steps to the pool in the rock.
Give us this day our daily bread
She swilled and cut
And laid psalms and blessings on her dish.

In the bay the waves pursued their indifferent dances.

In that poem, from Part 4 of Fishermen with Ploughs, *Jock has 'maybe one in a hundred chances'. The book, ultimately, is about what happens after a nuclear disaster. How many chances do you think we've got? As many as Jock, more or less?*
. . . I am a bit pessimistic . . . Still, you never know, we might be stronger than you think, in the spirit.

What do we need to do to improve our chances?
I really don't know. I have no idea. Just hope for the best.

This might be an appropriate moment for **Stations of the Cross:**

Our winter jar of grain and malt
Is a Lenten urn.

Lord, it is time. Take our yoke
And sunwards turn.

To drudge in furrows till you drop
Is to be born

Out of that mild mothering hill
And that chaste burn.

God-begun, the barley-rack
By man is borne.

Foldings of women. Your harrow sweat
Darkens her yarn.

Sower-and-seed, one flesh, you stumble
On stone and thorn.

You are bound for the kingdom of death. The enfolded
Women mourn.

Scythes are sharpened to bring you down,
King Barleycorn.

The flails creak. Golden coat
From kernel is torn.

The fruitful stones thunder around,
Quern on quern.

The last black hunger rages through you
With hoof and horn.

Mother, fold him from those furrows,
Your rapt bairn.

Angel, shepherd, king are kneeling, look,
In the door of the barn.

Is the process of re-living Christ's progress from Pilate to the Cross in these terms, perhaps, a way of proclaiming hunger for all that Christ means—that it is a hunger equal to the basic, literal hunger for food?
That would be very fair . . . I agree.

Why has the story of Saint Magnus meant so much to you?
Well, I think it's because it is such a marvellous story, as it's told in the *Orkneyinga Saga* which was composed in Iceland about the year 1300, and is an anthology of wonderful stories about Earls of Orkney for about three centuries. This, possibly, is the greatest story of them all, the story of Magnus and his cousin, Hakon, who were disputing about the islands. They were joint Earls . . . and they were first cousins. We're told that people made trouble between them. The whole story is so marvellous that I feel drawn to it again and again. In fact, I wrote a long novel—maybe too long . . . I try to draw a parallel with the twentieth century with some of the things that were happening, especially during the last war . . .

You seem to approve of the somewhat recklessly productive Alice Voar in Greenvoe.
Well, I wouldn't necessarily approve of her. But I rather like her. She is more of a caricature than a properly rounded character . . . Most of the characters in that novel are caricatures.

Do you think of women as 'seed-jars', 'walking wombs'?
When I am trying to be profound I do, but I recognise they are far more than that!

Greenvoe *has been described as an* Under Milk Wood *of Orkney.*
Yes, I know. It has been compared very unfavourably! I didn't think of *Milk Wood* at all when I was writing it, until the reviewers began to compare them. Much to my discredit!

You seem to have it in for progress. There's 'Operation Black Star' *in* Greenvoe, *and there are the girls in* Fishermen with Ploughs *who are 'nothing but giggles, lipstick, and gramophone records'. Is there anything positive to be said for progress?*
Oh, yes, I'm sure there's quite a lot to be said for it. I sort of over-emphasise things, I think, the things that you mentioned. For example, I wouldn't be here if it weren't for progress—medical science. I would have been dead about thirty years ago, because I had T.B. when I was still a young man. There's a lot to be said for it from that point of view, and, of course, we are all far better off. I think I have tended to romanticise the past a bit. It must have been a very hard life that the farmers and fishermen had in Orkney a hundred years and more ago.

You have recently written a poem as a memorial to William and Mareon Clark. Who are they?
They were the first recorded Stromnesians, because they built an inn at the end of the bay, towards the end of the sixteenth century. There must have been people in Stromness before that, but they are the first recorded ones . . . Of course, they would only have built an inn because there were ships calling at the harbour at Hamnavoe, going on to America.

Do you think we can introduce more consciousness of elemental things to the modern world?

Well, that is partly the task of the artists and poets, to keep reminding people of their roots, however far forward we go into the future. However progressive and forward-looking, they are never to forget their origins and beginnings . . . And, possibly, I try to do that as best I can.

Stromness, 26th September 1980

In Memoriam
William and Mareon Clark

Four hundred years since you both
Went, sundered, into the dark,
Hearts and hearthstone cold,
William and Mareon Clark.

Search for a stone in the kirkyard—
Nothing. Never a mark.
No-one knows where your bones lie,
William and Mareon Clark.

Even the inn you built
To hustle about the work
Of welcome and keeping, is vanished,
William and Mareon Clark.

Your door stood open wide
From the rising of the lark
To the pole of night, to all men,
William and Mareon Clark.

You gathered about your fires
The crew of the wintered barque
From Lisbon, or Brest, or Boston,
William and Mareon Clark.

The plainsong of the priest,
The paraphrase in the kirk,
Were you tangled in their rhythms,
William and Mareon Clark.

Tired, you'd put out the lamp,
Cover the fire, and hark!
A scatter of hooves on the cobbles,
William and Mareon Clark.

You did not live to see
On the steep dyked westward park
The merchants' houses rising,
William and Mareon Clark.

Tall houses hewn from granite,
Piers on the tidal mark,
Yawl and cobble noust-gathered,
William and Mareon Clark.

Your first eyes never saw
The boys from the crofts embark
For the Davis Straits and the whale-fling,
William and Mareon Clark.

Nor saw them come back in August,
Sovereigns sewn in each sark,
Salt men urgent for barley,
William and Mareon Clark.

Eighteenth-century wars,
The herring shoal and the shark
Dowered that shore with silver,
William and Mareon Clark.

Eighteenth-century wars,
Doubloon and kroner and mark,
Made later taverners rich,
William and Mareon Clark.

Graham and Gow and Millie—
You never drew the cork
For hero, pirate, spaewife,
    William and Mareon Clark.

Nothing. You cannot hear us.
Two names, quilled and stark
On a lawyer's parchment, ghostings—
    William and Mareon Clark.

Forgive this deluge of words,
First townsfolk, wherever you ark.
I have cut you dove-marks on stone:
    WILLIAM AND MAREON CLARK.

A Man Between Two Hills: Culloden

Where are you going from here, man?
I have a small free place at the shore.

What will you do after this day?
Be silent and hidden and poor.

Where are your friends tonight?
I left some tarrying on the moor.

What of your king waiting in France for news?
He listens. Strings are stroked, a modish
        heart-piercing air.

When will you rouse you, a stag, again?
When I hear the small knock of a girl at the door.

What cry in the mountains then?
Men seeking still the wolf's and the wildcat's lair.

Hamnavoe Market

No school today! We drove in our gig to the town.
Daddo bought us each a coloured balloon.
Mine was yellow, it hung high as the moon.
A cheapjack urged. Swingboats went up and down.

Cocoanuts, ice-cream, apples, ginger beer
Routed the five bright shillings in my pocket.
I won a bird-on-a-stick and a diamond locket.
The Blind Fiddler, the broken-nosed boxers were there.

The booths huddled like mushrooms along the pier.
I ogled a goldfish in its crystal cell.
Round every reeling corner came a drunk.

The sun whirled a golden hoof. It lingered. It fell
On a nest of flares. I yawned. Old Madge our mare
Homed through a night black as a bottle of ink.

Uranium

We passed through the Door of Stone.
We stayed a while, with tusks and ashes.
We left.
The stones fell, silently.

The Door of Bronze opened to us.
In the square
Masques were danced: battle, harvest, hunt.
Time dimmed those pillars.
The streets were empty.
The tribe had moved far on.

Always the Door of Salt
Had stood open.
We entered, returned with fish.
Quick thrustings, takings:
A few did not return.

The Green Door—
A man forged a key to that,
After burns, brimmings of iron music.
The barns lie fair to the sun.
Here
We have been citizens a winter or two.

This, we are assured,
Is not the place still
Where the tribe
Will write history on skins
And seal it in a jar, cave-kept.
A horseman
Returned across the desert this morning.
On the far side
He had stood before the magnificent Door of Fire.

George Mackay Brown
Orkney, 1980
Photographer: Jessie Ann Matthew

George Mackay Brown

George Mackay Brown was born in Stromness, Orkney, on 17th October 1921. His father was a postman (as was MacDiarmid's) and a part-time tailor. He attended Stromness Academy 1926-40, where at the age of seven or eight he dimly guessed at a gift for writing in class compositions. In 1941 he suffered an attack of tuberculosis which effectively kept him out of work for about ten years—a period used to the full—as Iain Crichton Smith had in a similar situation—in reading and writing. 1951-52 was spent at Newbattle Abbey College — where fellow-Orcadian Edwin Muir was Warden (as well as friend and mentor)—a year he has described as the happiest of his life. After another TB attack and another brief spell at Newbattle he entered Edinburgh University and graduated MA with Honours in English in 1960. From 1961 to 1962 he did post-graduate work on Gerard Manley Hopkins at Edinburgh; he then returned to Stromness, where he has lived ever since.

Awards: SAC grant 1965; Society of Authors Travel Award 1968 (visited Ireland); Katherine Mansfield short story award and Scottish Arts Council literature prize (both for *A Time to Keep*); hon. degrees from Open University (M.A.) and Dundee University (LL.D.); F.R.S.L.; O.B.E. 1974.

In addition to poetry George Mackay Brown writes novels, short stories, plays, and essays; he has recently been collaborating with the composer Peter Maxwell Davies who lives on Hoy.

Orkney—its people and history—is the centre of his life and work. He describes his themes thus: "mainly religious (birth, love, death, resurrection, ceremonies of fishing and agriculture)"; and his verse forms: "traditional stanza forms, sonnets, ballads, *vers libre,* prose poems, runes, choruses, etc"; his sources and influences: "Norse sagas, Bible stories, ritual and ceremony, writers like Brecht, Thomas Mann, Yeats."

Selected Publications

Poetry: *The Storm* (Orkney Press 1954—introduction by Edwin Muir); *Loaves and Fishes* (Hogarth 1959); *The Year of the Whale* (Hogarth 1965); *The Five Voyages of Arnor* (K. D. Duval 1966); *Fishermen with Ploughs* (Hogarth 1971); *Lifeboat and Other Poems* (Crediton: Gilbertson, 1971); *New and Selected Poems* (Hogarth 1971); *Winterfold* (Chatto/Hogarth 1976); *Selected Poems* (Hogarth 1977)

Anthologies: *Twelve Modern Scottish Poets,* ed. C. King (University of London Press 1971); *Penguin Modern Poets 21* (1972—with N. MacCaig and I. C. Smith); *Modern Scottish Poetry,* ed. M. Lindsay (Carcanet 1976)

Novels: *Greenvoe* (Hogarth 1972); *Magnus* (Hogarth 1973)

Stories: *A Calendar of Love* (Hogarth 1967); *A Time to Keep* (Hogarth 1969); *The Sun's Net* (Hogarth 1976); *Pictures in the Cave* (Chatto and Windus 1977—for children); *Six Lives of Fankle the Cat* (Chatto and Windus 1980—for children)

Plays: *A Spell for Green Corn* (Hogarth 1970)

Essays: *An Orkney Tapestry* (Gollancz 1969); *Letters from Hamnavoe* (Gordon Wright 1975); *Under Brinkie's Brae* (G. Wright 1979)

Critical studies: P. Pacey, " 'Finished fragrance': the poetry of George Mackay Brown", *Akros* 32, December 1976; Alan Bold, *George Mackay Brown* (Oliver & Boyd 1978)

See also: G. M. Brown, "An Autobiographical Essay" in *As I Remember: ten Scottish authors recall how writing began for them* , ed. M. Lindsay (Hale 1979)

Robert Garioch

Why do you write in Scots?
Well, it is my native tongue. It's as simple as that. I am not saying my native language—my native tongue. I remember the conscious effort I had to make at school to adapt my speech to the requirements of the teachers. This is different nowadays, because people don't speak as my father and mother did . . . They spoke Scots. That is to say, Scottish English, with a pretty good Scottish vocabulary. So that was the predicament I was conscious of—and I did it deliberately, as a reaction, almost, against a very English upbringing. I did Honours English, don't forget, at the University. Not Honours in anything but English. Rhetoric and English Literature—that was the name of the course.

Are you speaking to me now in the kind of language—or tongue—that you would use if you were speaking to someone you'd known a long time?
I am not very conscious of the way I speak just now at all. This is my normal speech . . . for any purposes whatsoever.

Your subjects range from Sisyphus, Faust, Robert Fergusson and Einstein to headmasters, worms and swans. The use of Scots certainly hasn't restricted your choice of subjects; but you are best known, I think, for a special gift of pawky satire, aren't you?
Yes. Well, it's one thing I do. I think people rather like it. It tends to appeal to people to hear somebody being ticked off. I do have a certain ability in that direction, I will admit, though there are other things that I can do. Will I read an example of my Gariochian satire? It's a new art form this, I invented. It's an elegy with a happy ending. I am

Robert Garioch (1978). Oil on canvas, 69 × 44½ inches

very proud of that. It's one of these Edinburgh Sonnets —**Elegy:**

They are lang deid, folk that I used to ken,
their firm-set lips aa mowdert and agley,
sherp-tempert een rusty amang the cley:
they are baith deid, thae wycelike, bienlie men,

heidmaisters, that had been in pouer for ten
or twenty year afore fate's taiglie wey
brocht me, a young, weill-hairnit, blate and fey
new-cleckit dominie, intill their den.

Ane tellt me it was time I learnt to write—
round-haund, he meant—and saw about my hair:
I mind of him, beld-heidit, wi a kyte.

Ane sneerit quarterly—I cuidna square
my savings bank—and sniftert in his spite.
Weill, gin they arena deid, it's time they were.

Another of these Edinburgh Sonnets—*Heard in the Gairdens*—is a rejoicing by someone set free from the necessity of earning a living.

You do often take up an anti-establishment stance in your poems, and you are also very interested in the theme of freedom, aren't you?

Yes. I seem to have a lot of difficulties in having my own way in the world and there are always plenty of organizations to prevent me from having it . . . Mind you, it's no use asking me to do anything to overthrow the establishment, that's another matter. I put up with it, but complain. I think that sums the whole thing up. Yes. I have got a poem about that—*The Percipient Swan.* It's not myself complaining in person, but a swan in a public park—Inverleith Park . . . And this swan has realised what's what, and doesn't like it—indeed has got a plan to do something about it, which is more than I have ever done . . .

You admire the swan, but you withhold your sympathy from poor old Sisyphus.

Ah, yes. Sisyphus is myself, I think, and I see through myself, but queerly . . . It's pretty merciless, I dare say, but when it was started it wasn't meant to be myself at all. It was a literary exercise, translating the untranslatable line of Homer. I'd been reading the 'Times Lit. Sup.', and they gave many examples of attempts to translate that line about the stone bumping down the hill. All failures—but, of course, they were all in English. So I tried it in Scots, and having written one line and being economical, I thought I'd better write some more . . . It turns out I'm the hero of it, but never mind. **Sisyphus:**

Bumpity doun in the corrie gaed whuddran the pitiless whun stane.
Sisyphus, pechan and sweitan, disjaskit, forfeuchan and broun'd-aff,
sat on the heather a hanlawhile, houpan the Boss didna spy him,
seein the terms of his contract includit nae mention of tea-breaks,
syne at the muckle big scunnersom boulder he trauchlit aince mair.
Ach! hou kenspeckle it was, that he ken'd ilka spreckle and blotch on't.
Heavin awa at its wecht, he manhaunnlit the bruitt up the brae-face,
takkan the easiest gait he had fand in a fudder of dour years,
haudan awa frae the craigs had affrichtit him maist in his youth-heid,
feelin his years aa the same, he gaed cannily, tenty of slipped discs.
Eftir an hour and a quarter he warslit his wey to the brae's heid,
hystit his boulder richt up on the tap of the cairn—and it stude there!
streikit his length on the chuckie-stanes, houpan the Boss wadna spy him,
had a wee look at the scenery, feenisht a pie and a cheese-piece.
Whit was he thinkin about, that he jist gied the boulder a wee shove?
Bumpity doun in the corrie gaed whuddran the pitiless whun stane,
Sisyphus dodderan eftir it, shair of his cheque at the month's end.

I suppose Sisyphus collaborates in his own degradation, to

be sure of his cheque at the month's end—a case, perhaps, of misplaced ingenuity. But you approve ingenuity of another kind in 'The Canny Hen'.
Yes, indeed. This is a hen, an intelligent hen, which, or rather who discovered it was possible to eat the yolks out of the eggs . . . a battery hen, you must understand.

'Fredome is a noble thing,' but it can be disconcerting at times, when something else has it . . . and the poet doesn't have as much as he would like.
Yes, quite so. This is the wood-worm and dry-rot poem . . . When these wood-beetles begin to exercise their prerogative, that's a bit much . . . It's called **A Matter of Life and Death.** Nothing to do with my house—I'd better make that very clear.

My useful dead possessions come alive,
no use to me, though I suppose they have

fun at my expense. See, a bit of my door,
turned to wood-beetle, flying past your ear.

Haven't I paid for it, part of my house?
What right has it to put out wings and whizz?

Joists and rafters, sifting through the air:
"Look out!" says life, "my spores are everywhere."

Old sapwood timbers, wickedest for lust,
blow up mushroom-shaped clouds of bright red dust.

The organism's getting inchoate;
riot police are squirting creosote.

In solidarity, their trouser-seats
fly off to Ossett in the shape of moths.

Mansions are on the move; squatter and soldier
evacuate their posts, shoulder to shoulder.

Now that organic matter's in full flush
of victory, can we trust our own flesh?

We're told that Herod's maggots jumped the gun
while he was still, officially, live man.

So Herod, though no Christian, in his way
had life, and had it more abundantly.

Bourgeois reactionary, I would have
my maggots after, not before, the grave.

Why should my things now give themselves such airs?
What right have chairs, floors, tables, dadoes, doors

to go off on their own? At any rate,
my teeth stay loyal to their plastic plate.

There is wit in that poem, of course, but it is also a serious poem, isn't it? It is a matter of life and death, and the theme of freedom is very much a matter of life and death in your long poem, **The Wire.** *Does this interest in themes of freedom and captivity owe something to your time as a prisoner of war in the second World War?*
Yes. To prisoners the wire is something with an existence—I can't explain it exactly. It seems to have an existence of its own. It's *the* wire, not just any wire. And it's all round, of course.

This is round the prison camp.
Yes. And inside the wire, there is a small wire called the trip wire, and you mustn't touch that, because there's a sentry with a rifle, and he would shoot you. Not in Italy, but in Germany. In Germany you did exactly what you were supposed to do . . . I was in both places. Italy wasn't so bad—I liked the Italians, rather. It has happened that I borrowed a bayonet from the guard in order to open a tin—but Germany's a very serious and different matter. And this is a very serious poem. This is an extract from it, about those guards. They have orders—the usual business with soldiers—they have exact orders . . . to shoot to kill . . . and they did. There was no messing about. So, how were you to think of them? But, of course, you don't know them. They don't know who you are; it's just carrying out an order.

This poem is not exactly about the POW camp. It's about a planet which has wires strung all over it, like those wires in the desert that marked the mine-fields, with triangular bits of tin hanging on them. So, you see, there are different memories mixed up together. This bit is about the guards:

Impersonal in uniform,
the guairds are neither friens nor faes;
nane ettles to propitiate
nor fashes them wi bribes or praise.

Efficient and predictable,
they cairry out their orders stricht;
here naething happens unforeseen;
it is jist sae, no wrang nor richt.

On this dour mechanistic muir
wi nae land's end, and endless day,
whaur nae thing thraws a shadow, here
the truth is clear, and it is wae.

The crouds that thrang the danger-spots
weill ken what wey their warld's wrocht,
but aye the mair they pauchle on
to win release frae nigglin thocht.

Some pairts the pattern of the Wire
leaves clear for fifty yairds and mair
whaur soil has crined to desert stuir
wi scroggie bussels puir and bare.

Here some folk wycer nor the lave
or maybe suiner gien to skar
tether theirsels wi chains to stakes,
sae they may gang, but no owre far.

Birlan in wretchedness aroun
their safe lives' centre, they maun dree
temptation sair to break their chains
for aye they ettle to gang free.

Some stark and strang stravaig their yird
like shelties that hae never taen
the bit; mere smeddum drives them on,
their lives are short, but are their ain.

Are you saying that the bid for freedom must be made, that a short life is preferable to 'birlan in wretchedness'?
I think, yes—otherwise the word 'wretchedness' wouldn't have such stress laid upon it. But it's a difficult thing to say exactly what I'm saying. I am giving the different options without saying too much about it.

You have enjoyed translating many of the poems of Giuseppe Belli into Scots . . .
I've had great fun with Belli—and indeed, he is great fun; but just for once I'd like to read a serious, very feeling poem about a poor family in Rome. Just a contradiction to the general idea that people have of him as a rather rough and wild comic sonneteer. **The Puir Faimly:**

Wheesht nou, my darling bairnies, bide ye quaet:
yir faither's comin suin, jist bide a wee.
Oh Virgin of the greitin, please help me,
Virgin of waymenting, ye that can dae't.

My hairts, I wuss that ye cuid ken hou great
my luve is! Dinnae greit, or I sall dee.
He'll bring us something hame wi him, you'll see,
and we will get some breid, and ye will eat . . .

Whit's that ye're saying, Joe? jist a wee while,
my son, ye dinnae like the dark ava.
Whit can I dae fir ye, if there's nae yle?

Puir Lalla, whit's the maitter? Oh my bairn,
ye're cauld? But dinnae staund agin the waa:
come and I'll warm ye on yir mammie's airm.

Do you have any special favourites among your works?
Yes, the translations I did from George Buchanan's Latin tragedies **Jephthah** and **The Baptist.** This is my favourite among my books, which may seem strange, because, of course, it is a translation. However, that's the way of it . . . There is something very curious about the endings of both of these plays. They seem to give a little bit of Christian hope, and at the very end that hope seems to be rather put aside, I feel . . . Well, the Baptist has been duly put to death and the messenger comes with a word of hope, and this is what he says:

If daith is maitter for weeping, let us wepe for the deid
whase anerlie hope is buried wi the body,
wha traist-na that eftir brief time o sleeping
their bodies sall come back to life again,
to live anither and a better life.
Let miserable men wepe for the deid;
fate can mak nae man miserable:
for tho baith innocent and sinfu sowls
come alike to the ending o their lives,
nane sall dee badly, wha hae levit weill:
if ye judge a man's misery by his mainner of pairting,
ye maun think sae monie halie faithers miserable
wha were reivit o life by the reuch sea,
by fire, or cauld steel, or on the cross.
For him wha dees a disciple o the sooth,
for religion or for the Faither's laws,
we suld be glaid at his gude ending
and grein for a like pairting frae our life.

(and the Chorus replies)

It is certain that aa ye hae said is true,
but we, betrayit by opinions and errors,
while fleeing fate, rin foolishly on fate.
Tho fire may spare us, we droun in the sea;
if we perish nat by water, the plague will kill us;
the war's survivor is wastit by slaw disease.
God may defer, but doesna cancel our fate,
and we pey daily interest for daith's delay,
in dule and danger, trauchle and disease.
Nor is a lang life ocht but a lang chain
o evils; even to the term o daith,
linked in a langsom series. We are laith to think
we are in thralldom, thirlit to yon chain;
and the outgait frae whilk we micht win free
skars us mair nor the slavery.

Do you yourself hold with the note of Christian hope, or do you hold with the qualifications that follow?
I am not quite sure, and I wonder if George Buchanan was sure either.

Edinburgh, 28th September 1980

Jephthah

Scene IV

Oh, ruler o the gowden licht,
sun, wha swees the lyft aroun,
swith returning day and nicht,
wha bear your never-bydand flame,
pairting the seasons for the warld,
eftir twenty darksom years
nou we see your blissit licht,
Isaac's sons at last set free
frae the dule o slavery.
Jephthah's strang richt haund has brak
Ammon's hairt for aa his pride,
the reiver reivit o his gear.
His bowmen were nae gude til him
for aa the shafts that they lat flee,
his chariots o puckle use
for aa their curving sickle-blades.
Neither his wecht o heavy horse
nor serried schiltrouns o wicht men
could haud agen the pouer o God.
Nou, ye heathen, ken for shair
that God is neither stock nor stane,
nae skeelie carver hackit him
wi airn chisel frae the block,
nae potter's souple finger-knebbs
shapit him frae slochent cley
in the semblance o man's face:
God, our God bides evermair
abune, wi battlements o flame,
he wha has made aa things that be,
whase safety is a certainty,
omnipotent in majesty,
he isna easy to be seen,
nor willing that a mortal haund
suld scrieve his likeness faithfully.
He curbs the frantic pride o kings,
absolute in his richteousness,
he brings their wicked vows til nocht,
and founers their owreweening hopes
o swelling up their ain conceit:

he lifts the puir man frae the stour,
wha used to tend his stinkan flock,
he sets on the herd-laddie's heid
the precious royal diadem
and thrings intil his muckle neive
the gowden sceptre o the king.
The fabric o the daedal warld
acknowledges him Lord and God
allanerlie in ilka airt,
luves him and worships in eterne:
whatever things the orient sun
beats doun upon wi brennan rays,
whatever, at the hicht o noon,
lowes aneath his nearer flames,
whatever frae the Tagus drinks
yon noble river's tawny bree,
and he condemned to bide in airts
amang the snaws that never melt.
Ye Hebrew lassies, busk ye nou;
mak yoursels braw wi Indian gems,
scaitter about ye bonny flures
o ilka colour ye can find.
Whaur are aa your jowan cymbals,
why nae souns o lyres and clarsachs?
Sing a new sang til the Lord,
wha has wrocht our victory.
Why is it ye dinna blaw
the chanter wi its monie holes,
wha will dance a fowersom neatly?
Let's forget our times o trauchle
ane and aa and aathegither.
Wale out the leader o the flock
as an altar-offering;
let Arabian incense burn
reekin up in fragrant clouds.
Iphis, dochter o the chief,
ye, the hope o this great clan,
busk ye in your finest braws,
welcome back wi halie joy
your faither safe hame frae the wars.
Cleid you nou in purpie robes,
braid your bonnie gowden hair;
hear the shouting o the crowd:
here he is, your faither, himsel.

The Baptist — Scene XIII

Toures o Jerusalem, ye realm o Dauvid,
city o Solomon in aa his glory,
why siccan cankert rage agen the richteous,
siccan fell thirst for blude o halie prophets?
She wha suld be the rule o gudelie leving
is the true gless and mirour o transgressing:
hamesucken, bludeshed, treachery and reiving,
these are your schules' diurnal exercises.
Even the piety o priests and prelates
doesna dissuade them frae their wicked cunning.
Turning til idols nou, the folks abandon
God the almichtie Faither o Creation,
sairving as God things wrocht o stane and timber,
for thae the altars reik wi sacrifices;
carvers adore what they theirsels hae shapit,
lawlessly seeking life in lumps o maitter,
preeing dumb stocks to gie them spoken answers,
weill-plenisht lords beseeching serfs and paupers:
auncient observances gae doun in ruin.
Ye, by the blude o the unskaithfu prophets,
hailit sall be afore the great Tribunal:
wedows and puir folk cry aloud to Hevin,
plainting agen ye.
Doutless, for-thy, the punishment o vengeance
hings owre your heids, but-gif I'm faur misguidit.
For he wha dings the arrogant, and judges
Hevin and yird and ocean, the Omniscient,
sees frae abune the weping o his nation,
keeping in mind their prayers and waymenting,
and wi his strang richt haund will swithlie punish
sae great iniquity: he sall owreharle
weill-biggit bartizans wherein ye boasted:
barbarous conquerers sall hae your fairm-land,
your vineyard keepers gie the fruit to strangers:
here whaur the Temple rises nou to Hevin,

reaping his hairst, sall come the fremmit fairmer.
For-thy while yet the Deity's forebearance
leaves ye a hanlawhile to be repentant,
gie owre the vices o your wicked leving,
cast out the rites o fremmit idol-worship,
maister your greedy thirst for blude o kindred
and your unhalie hankering for riches.
But if ye winna turn ye in repentance,
cast out the rites o fremmit idol-worship,
maister your greedy thirst for blude o kindred
and your unhalie hankering for riches:
syne sall the wasting pestilence reduce ye,
hunger and dearth and war consume your fatness,
till wi your ain hairts' blude ye thole the peyment
richly deservit.

The Guid Faimly

Faither wins hame, my grannie leaves her wheel,
puir sowl, gies owre her spinning for the nicht:
she lays the buird, blaws her bit coal alicht,
and we sit-in to sup our puckle kail.

We mak oursels an omelet, aince in a while,
gey thin, sae's ye can fairly see the licht
throu it, jist like it wes a lug: aa richt,
we chaw a puckle nuts, and that's our meal.

While Faither and mysel and Clementine
bide on, she clears the buird, gaes ben and redds
the kitchie, and we hae a drappie wine.

The wee carafe timmit doun til the dregs,
a wee pish, a hailmary said, and syne
lither and lown, we sclim intill our beds.

Giuseppe Belli No. 287 *La bona famija* 28 novembre 1831.
Translated by Robert Garioch with the help of Antonia Stott.

Robert Garioch Edinburgh, 1980
Photographer: Jessie Ann Matthew

Robert Garioch

Robert Garioch Sutherland, to use his full name, was born in Edinburgh on 9th May 1909 to Scots-speaking parents. His father was a painter and semi-professional fiddler and his mother was a music teacher. He was educated at the Royal High School, and at Edinburgh University (1927-31, earning extra money as a cinema pianist) where he graduated MA with Honours in English. In the Second World War he served with the Royal Signals; was a POW in Italy and Germany 1942-45, an experience recounted in *Two Men and a Blanket: Memoirs of Captivity* (Southside 1975). He taught in schools in Edinburgh, London, and Kent, until his retirement. He was Writer in Residence at Edinburgh University 1971-73, and has worked as a lexicographer's orraman on the *Dictionary of the Older Scottish Tongue* and as a transcriber with the School of Scottish Studies. He was an editorial advisor to *Scottish International* 1968-74, and has recently been Poet in Residence to Radio Forth.

Awards: Sloan Prize for Verse in Scots 1930; SAC award 1968.

The bulk of Garioch's work is in Scots. His family spoke Scots and he was early influenced by A. D. Mackie's *Poems in Two Tongues.* He regarded his poems in Scots in much the same way as Allan Ramsay had seen his work, as a reaction—against 'englishness'. On his work he has commented: "Like everyone else, I suffer more or less from belonging to a half-nation betrayed to and taken over by the English government of 1707. So there is a political reason for writing Scots, but poetical reasons come first in poetry, I hope". His (superb) verse-craft and fluent command of Scots are usually put to the service of fantasy and satire, very often on Edinburgh life and manners; although he has also attempted a 'scientific poem', *The Muir,* in Scots. In a review of the *Collected Poems* Stephen Mulrine wrote, "Garioch is always a delight to read. Where craftsmanship matters, in the handling of the medium, so that an artificial language seems as natural as breathing, he has no peer among Lallans-users."

Garioch has also made vigorous translations into Scots of Pindar and Belli.

Selected Publications

Poetry: *17 poems for 6d: in Gaelic, Lowland Scots and English* (Edinburgh: Chalmers Press 1940—with Sorley MacLean); *Chuckies on the Cairn* (Chalmers Press 1949); *Selected Poems* (Macdonald 1966); *The Big Music* (Caithness Books 1971); *Doktor Faust in Rose Street* (Macdonald/Lines Review 1973); *Collected Poems* (Macdonald 1977, Carcanet 1980)

Anthologies: *Twelve Modern Scottish Poets,* ed. C. King (University of London Press 1971); *Modern Scottish Poetry,* ed. M. Lindsay (Carcanet 1976); *Modern Scots Verse,* ed. A. Scott (Akros 1978)

Autobiographical: *Two Men and a Blanket: Memoirs of Captivity* (Southside 1975)

Translation: *Jephtha* and *The Baptist* by George Buchanan (Oliver and Boyd 1957)

Play: *The Masque of Edinburgh* (Macdonald 1954)

Edited: *Made in Scotland: an anthology of fourteen Scottish poets* (Carcanet 1974)

Critical studies: R. Watson, "The speaker in the gairdens: the poetry of Robert Garioch", *Akros* 16, April 1971; E. Morgan, "The poet and the particle", *Essays* (1974); S. Mulrine, review of *Collected Poems* in *Akros* 36, December 1977

See also: R. Garioch, "Early days in Edinburgh", *As I Remember: ten Scottish authors recall how writing began for them,* ed. M. Lindsay (Hale 1979)

Overleaf: **Sorley MacLean** (1979)
Pencil, 23½ × 15¾ inches

Sorley MacLean (Somhairle MacGill-Eain)

It's been suggested that the number of people capable of understanding your work in the original is about 40. Do you think that's true?
Oh, no. There are far more than 40—and, of course, understanding is susceptible of a lot of degrees and varieties.

Would you agree that the audience is, perforce, limited?
The audience is very limited, yes.

Is that something that worries you?
No, it doesn't worry me in the least . . . I am writing for no audience. My idea of poetry is that a person should be as if he were talking to himself. It is dangerous to be conscious that you are talking to yourself—to get a kind of intellectual consciousness of talking to yourself. I think it should be a kind of spontaneous talking to oneself. . .

Are you proselytising for Gaelic?
Well, perhaps I began . . . You see, as I have said often before, I was one of the few of a family of tradition-bearers, especially of song, who had some of the finest Gaelic songs. I was about the only one of the whole lot of them who couldn't sing! It may be that subconsciously there came into my being the feeling that poetry is the next best thing. And I suppose when I started there was a kind of unconscious proselytisation.

When you write in Gaelic, though, you are really doing what comes naturally.
Yes. I was writing quite a lot of verse in my late teens in Gaelic and English. My English stuff was in the manner of the early Eliot and the Pound of *Hugh Selwyn Mauberley*. At a certain juncture, when I was about twenty, I realised it wasn't myself, that it was no good at all, and I stopped writing verse in English altogether. At that time, also, I was obsessed with the possibility that a time would come

when the great Gaelic songs—I don't say all Gaelic songs of all periods are great; some are awful—but I was obsessed with the time when there would be nobody left to hear them properly, because you cannot hear a song properly without knowing the language. And I think that my sense of inferiority about myself musically had quite a bit to do with it.

Would you like to see Gaelic more vigorously taught in Scotland?
Well, there has been quite a big change in the last ten years, and I hope that will continue . . . I think it probably will. A lot depends on the success of what they are doing in the outer isles. Of course, before that, there came the possibility of having much more Gaelic taught in secondary schools—that came in 1968. Now that has been followed by a great increase in the teaching of Gaelic in primary schools in Gaelic-speaking areas, of which the two chief protagonists are John Murray and Findlay MacLeod in Lewis. I think something will come of that, but at the same time I would like to see a greater increase in the teaching of it in secondary schools. The two have to go together.

Your poems are full of love: love of person and of place . . . I would like to have the pleasure of hearing you read **The Blue Rampart: Am Mùr Gorm**
I will read a translation. There is one thing to remember: the 'Tree of Strings' is an old kenning for the harp. It's a tree of harp strings, and therefore it is a kind of symbol for music, and, perhaps by extension, for poetry. There is another difficulty about it, because there is an oxymoron at the end of the word 'Summit', because the word used in Gaelic is *creachainn,* which means 'bare summit' or 'bare wind-swept summit', and, of course, using the word 'summit' with the word 'luxuriant' doesn't bring out the oxymoron . . . but it's an inevitable thing in translation . . .

But for you the Cuillin would be
an exact and serrated blue rampart
girdling with its march-wall
all that is in my fierce heart.

But for you the sand
that is in Talisker compact and white
would be a measureless plain to my expectations
and on it the spear desire would not turn back.

But for you the oceans
in their unrest and their repose
would raise the wave-crests of my mind
and settle them on a high serenity.

And the brown brindled moorland
and my reason would co-extend—
but you imposed on them an edict
above my own pain.

And on a distant luxuriant Summit
there blossomed the Tree of Strings,
among its leafy branches your face,
my reason and the likeness of a star.

Mur b'e thusa bhiodh an Cuilithionn
'na mhùr eagarra gorm
ag crioslachadh le bhalla-crìche
na tha 'nam chridhe borb.

Mur b'e thusa bhiodh a' ghaineamh
tha 'n Talasgar dùmhail geal
'na clàr biothbhuan do mo dhùilean,
air nach tilleadh an rùn-ghath.

'S mur b'e thusa bhiodh na cuantan
'nan luasgan is 'nan tàmh
a' togail càir mo bhuadhan,
'ga cur air suaimhneas àrd.

'S bhiodh am monadh donn riabhach
agus mo chiall co-shìnt'—
ach chuir thusa orra riaghladh
os cionn mo phianaidh fhìn.

Agus air creachainn chéin fhàsmhoir
chinn blàthmhor Craobh nan Teud,
'na meangach duillich t' aodann,
mo chiall is aogas réil.

John MacInnes has said that the two major characteristics of your poetry are a concern with ideals of politics and society, and the other a concern expressed in love poems. These two concerns meet, separate, meet again thoughout your work. Do you think this is so?
Yes, to a great extent, especially poems of a certain period . . . most of them, probably.

In the early volume, Poems to Eimhir, *there's a poem about figures of great importance in history, Christ and Lenin. Your response to these figures becomes involved in your response to a loved one.*

The Turmoil: Am Buaireadh

Never has such turmoil
nor vehement trouble been put in my flesh
by Christ's suffering on the earth
or by the millions of the skies.

And I took no such heed of a vapid dream—
green wood of the land of story—
as when my stubborn heart leaped to the glint
of her smile and golden head.

And her beauty cast a cloud
over poverty and a bitter wound
and over the world of Lenin's intellect,
over his patience and his anger.

Cha do chuir de bhuaireadh riamh
no thrioblaid dhian 'nam chré
allaban Chrìosda air an talamh
no muillionan nan speur.

'S cha d'ghabh mi suim de aisling bhaoith—
coille uaine tìr an sgeòil—
mar leum mo chridhe rag ri tuar
a gàire's cuailein òir.

Agus chuir a h-àilleachd sgleò
air bochdainn's air creuchd sheirbh
agus air saoghal tuigse Leninn,
air fhoighidinn's air fheirg.

The musical element is very strong in Gaelic poetry, isn't it?
It is in the sense that until recently, this century, most Gaelic poetry actually could be sung, but, of course, in the nineteenth century people like William Livingstone started long poems that were not to be sung. But I suppose that on the whole there is a very great emphasis on the actual sound of the poetry.

Does that apply to your own?
Yes. In fact it applied to most Gaelic poetry until this century, but there's some this century where it doesn't apply . . I would have said that the primary sensuousness of Gaelic poetry is of the ear, that it has been, traditionally. Mind you, there are some great things in, say, the eighteenth-century poetry of MacDonald and the poetry of Macintyre where you get a great visual and tactile sensuousness . . but I think even then sound is predominant.

When you're writing a poem, then, I suppose you pay more attention to the cadencing of lines, the sonic effects of words than a poet writing in English might do.
I would say that I do. There's a fair variety, I think, technically, in my stuff, and I go from almost free verse to a very different type . . . Of course, Gaelic is, I think, metrically very flexible, except that it's not at all happy with regular iambics. There's another thing about Gaelic. I think Gaelic's strongest point syntactically is that it's awfully good at indicating places and degrees of emphasis by natural inversions which you could use in ordinary speech, and various types of particles. That's one of the things that makes Gaelic especially difficult to translate into English, because English has to a certain extent lost its capacity for that . . . Inversions are generally artificial in English.

Gaelic has a great range of sound . . . I always maintain that the Celtic languages are fundamentally mid-European languages which have some of the characteristics of the Teutonic and Nordic languages, and of the Mediterranean languages, especially Latin. After all, the Celts were, I suppose, a mid-European people . . . Scottish Gaelic has kept the range of vowels better than Irish Gaelic.

It's been said that your poetic voice is very much in the authentic tradition of Gaelic poetry in Scotland—or, indeed, in Ireland. You are also a modern in that you bring together the apparently disparate elements of love and politics, personal passion and social responsibility. In 'The Choice', *for example, you seem to be saying that personal success in love must be earned by participation in the human community.*
Well, I'm not actually saying that. I'm saying that it would be desirable that it should be, but actually it's not. **The Choice: An Roghainn**

I walked with my reason
out beside the sea.
We were together but it was
keeping a little distance from me.

Then it turned saying:
is it true you heard
that your beautiful white love
is getting married early on Monday?

I checked the heart that was rising
in my torn swift breast
and I said: most likely;
why should I lie about it?

How should I think that I would grab
the radiant golden star,
that I would catch it and put it
prudently in my pocket?

I did not take a cross's death
in the hard extremity of Spain
and how then should I expect
the one new prize of fate?

I followed only a way
that was small, mean, low, dry, lukewarm,
and how then should I meet
the thunderbolt of love?

But if I had the choice again
and stood on that headland,
I would leap from heaven or hell
with a whole spirit and heart.

Choisich mi cuide ri mo thuigse
a-muigh ri taobh a'chuain;
bha sinn còmhla ach bha ise
a' fuireach tiotan bhuam.

An sin thionndaidh i ag ràdha:
a bheil e fìor gun cual
thu gu bheil do ghaol geal àlainn
a' pòsadh tràth Di-luain?

Bhac mi 'n cridhe bha 'g éirigh
'nam bhroilleach reubte luath
is thubhairt mi: tha mi cinnteach;
carson bu bhriag e bhuam?

Ciamar a smaoinichinn gun glacainn
an rionnag leugach òir,
gum beirinn oirre's cuirinn i
gu ciallach 'na mo phòc?

Cha d' ghabh mise bàs croinn-ceusaidh
ann an éiginn chruaidh na Spàinn
is ciamar sin bhiodh dùil agam
ri aon duais ùir an dàin?

Cha do lean mi ach an t-slighe chrìon
bheag ìosal thioram thlàth,
is ciamar sin a choinnichinn
ri beithir-theine ghràidh?

Ach nan robh'n roghainn rithist dhomh
's mi 'm sheasamh air an àird,
leumainn á neamh no iutharna
le spiorad 's cridhe slàn.

You wrote a good deal of what you might call poetry of social consciousness during the thirties.
Yes, and since, I think.

The rage of a man devoted to social justice is magnificently turned into poetry in 'A Highland Woman'. *The poem focuses on Christian hypocrisies, doesn't it?*

I was thinking of the fact that this extreme Calvinism postulated that only a tiny minority even of the people who followed the Church would get anything but an eternity of physical and mental torture . . . The fact that the Church said, this is only a vale of tears so what does it matter, yet eternity was to be pretty bleak for the vast majority even of the Church's adherents. **A Highland Woman: Ban-Ghàid -heal**

By the way, 'Black Labour' refers to the days of work that had to be done for the landlord partly in lieu of rent, then it came to mean any hard work in the fields, and quite a lot of that devolved on women, because the men would be away at fishing, perhaps, at the time of a lot of hard spring work and autumn work. Even when I was young it was quite common to see prematurely aged women because of that.

Hast Thou seen her, great Jew,
who art called the One Son of God?
Hast Thou seen on Thy way the like of her
labouring in the distant vineyard?

The load of fruits on her back,
a bitter sweat on brow and cheek,
and the clay basin heavy on the back
of her bent poor wretched head.

Thou hast not seen her, Son of the carpenter,
who art called the King of Glory,
among the rugged western shores
in the sweat of her food's creel.

This Spring and last Spring
and every twenty Springs from the beginning,
she has carried the cold seaweed
for her children's food and the castle's reward.

And every twenty Autumns gone
she has lost the golden summer of her bloom,
and the Black Labour has ploughed the furrow
across the white smoothness of her forehead.

And Thy gentle church has spoken
about the lost state of her miserable soul,
and the unremitting toil has lowered
her body to a black peace in a grave.

And her time has gone like a black sludge
seeping through the thatch of a poor dwelling:
the hard Black Labour was her inheritance;
grey is her sleep to-night.

Am faca Tu i, Iùdhaich mhóir,
ri 'n abrar Aon Mhac Dhé?
Am fac' thu 'coltas air Do thriall
ri strì an fhìon-lios chéin?

An cuallach mhiosan air a druim,
fallus searbh air mala is gruaidh;
's a' mhios chreadha trom air cùl
a cinn chrùibte bhochd thruaigh.

Chan fhaca Tu i, Mhic an t-saoir,
ri 'n abrar Rìgh na Glòir,
a miosg nan cladach carrach siar,
fo fhallus cliabh a lòin.

An t-earrach so agus so chaidh
's gach fichead earrach bho 'n an tùs
tharruing ise 'n fheamainn fhuar
chum biadh a cloinne 's duais an tùir.

'S gach fichead foghar tha air triall
chaill i samhradh buidh nam blàth;
is threabh an dubh-chosnadh an clais
tarsuinn mìnead ghil a clàir.

Agus labhair T' eaglais chaomh
mu staid chaillte a h-anama thruaigh;
agus leag an cosnadh dian
a corp gu sàmhchair dhuibh an uaigh.

Is thriall a tìm mar shnighe dubh
a' drùdhadh tughaidh fàrdaich bochd;
mheal ise an dubh-chosnadh cruaidh;
is glas a cadal suain an nochd.

Many modern poets have separated reason from feeling. There's Eliot's coinage, 'dissociation of sensibility'; Yeats separated perfection of the life from perfection of the work; Wallace Stevens elevates an imperialist imagination as a disembodied faculty of perception. But you seem to insist on the unity of reason and feeling. They are constantly in danger of splitting off from each other, but you are emphatic that they mustn't be divided. Is that true, do you think?
It is certainly true of myself. I can admire poetry that separates them . . . but that type of poetry is not for me.

In spite of any modern horror, in spite of any prompting to despair you may find you remain, in the largest sense, adamantly romantic. I don't mean to suggest that you are just doggedly romantic. You seem to find it possible to continue to have faith in the things in which you believe, whatever may be served up by the horror of the century or the idiocy of man.
Well, I would say myself something that has been much better said by Wordsworth in his sonnet *To Toussaint L'Ouverture:*

> "Thy friends are exultations, agonies,
> And love, and man's unconquerable mind."

I believe in the greatness of the human spirit.

Skye, 22nd September 1980

Translations of poems are Sorley MacLean's own. They are reproduced from the bilingual edition of his poems 'Spring tide and Neap tide/Reothairt is Contraigh: Selected Poems/Taghadh de Dhàin, 1932-72' (Canongate 1977).

Sorley MacLean (1979)
Charcoal on paper
29½ x 21¾ inches

Eaglais Chatharra

Tha eaglais chatharra 'na cheann
Ag éigheach mu chor nan daoine
Agus mu chor gach creutair
A tha fulang pian na feòla
Agus goirteas an spioraid
Ris an can sinn an cridhe.

Tha i cnàmhan fad na tìde
Nuair nach eil i ag éigheach
Mu 'n nighinn ionraic 'sa chansair
'S mu 'n t-siùrsaich 'na h-eucail,
Mu 'n mhartair air inneal-ciùrraidh
Agus a chliù am bial na bréige.

Tha a glaodh air mullach beinne
Agus mùchte 's an t-suil-chruthaich
Anns a' bhial nach fhaigh an éisdeachd,
Mu 'n t-saoi 's mu 'n churaidh gun ainm
'S mu 'n mhartair nach cluinnear sgeul air.

Tha sùil gun chadal gun tàmh
Air an truaghan ionraic chlaoidhte
'S air a' mhurtair chaothaich
Nach do dh' iarr a bhreith,
Air maodal theann an leanaibh
'S i gu sgàineadh leis a' ghort;
Air a' chalar sgreamhaidh
'S air a' chansair oillteil,
Air cràdh do-ghiùlan aona chreutair.

Air na seòmraichean gas,
Air gach Belsen a bh' ann,
Air bom an dadmuin is an neodroin
'S air an léirchreach nach fhaigh cainnt.

A Church Militant

There is a church militant in his head
shouting about the condition of man
and about the state of every creature
that is suffering the pain of the flesh
and the soreness of the spirit,
which we call the heart.

It is girning all the time
when it is not shouting
about the innocent girl in cancer
and about the whore in her disease,
about the martyr on a rack
and his repute in the lying mouth.

Its cry is on the top of a mountain
and smothered in the quagmire
in the mouth that gets no hearing,
about the good man and the hero nameless
and about the martyr of whom there is no tale.

Its eye is without sleep or peace
on the innocent oppressed poor creature
and on the insane murderer
who did not ask to be born,
on the child's belly
almost splitting with famine;
on the loathsome cholera
and on the horrific cancer,
on the intolerable pain of one creature.

On the gas chambers,
on every Belsen that was,
on the atom and neutron bomb
and on the utter destruction that has no words.

Iadhshlat

Tha lethchiad bliadhna on bhuain
Mi iadhshlat air a sàilleabh,
Dha mo shròin is dha mo shùil,
Iomhaigh chùbhraidh a bòidhche,
Fada fada mun do thuig mi
Gu bheil an gaol cho féineil
'S gun dall e sùilean an spioraid
Le aoibhneas sùil na feòla.

Dà fhichead bliadhna on chuireadh
Truaighe nan truaighe r' a bòidhche,
Agus on thug mi saor dh' a spiorad
Buaidh nam buadh nach robh air idir,
Colainn bhòidheach is spiorad uasal
Glant' an teine na truaighe.

Thuig mi an uair sin rud eile
Nach do thuig mi roimhe,
Mar a loisgeas an truaighe
Ròs is iadhshlat a' ghaoil,
Luibhean mìlse na colainn
Piocte le croman na truaighe,
'S gum fàs gaol cridhe á gaol feòla
Agus gun toir an gaol cridhe
Buaidh dhiomain air cor na feòla.

Honeysuckle

There are fifty years since I plucked
honeysuckle because of her,
for my nose and for my eye,
a fragrant image of her beauty,
long, long before I understood
that love is so selfish
that it will blind the eyes of the spirit
with the joy of the eye of the flesh.

Forty years since the misery
of miseries was added to her beauty,
and since I freely gave her spirit
the grace of graces that it did not have,
a beautiful body and a noble spirit
purified in the fire of misery.

I then understood another thing
that I did not understand before,
how misery burns
the rose and honeysuckle of love,
the plants of the sweetness of the body
plucked with the dibble of misery,
and that heart love will grow from flesh love
and that heart love has
a transitory victory over the condition of the flesh.

Sorley MacLean (1978). Pastel on coloured paper, 20 × 20½ inches

Dàn

(le John Cornford, air a chur an Gàidhlig)

A chridhe 'n t-saoghail gun chridhe,
A ghaoil cridhe, 's e mo smuain
Ortsa 'm pian ri mo thaobh,
An sgàil fhuarraidh do mo shùil.

Tha ghaoth ag éirigh feasgar,
Comharradh foghar a bhith faisg.
Tha eagal ormsa do chall,
Tha eagal orm roimh m' fhiamh.

A' mhìle mu dheireadh gu Huesca,
An fheansa mu dheireadh roimh ar n-uaill,
Biodh do smuain coibhneil, a ghaoil,
Gur saoileam nach eil thu bhuam.

'S ma leagas mìshealbh mo neart
Anns an uaigh staoin,
Cuimhnich nas urrainn dhut dhe 'n mhath;
Na dìochuimhnich mo ghaol.

Heart of the heartless world,
Dear heart, the thought of you
Is the pain at my side,
The shadow that chills my view.

The wind rises in the evening,
Reminds that autumn is near.
I am afraid to lose you,
I am afraid of my fear.

On the last mile to Huesca,
The last fence for our pride,
Think so kindly, dear, that I
Sense you at my side.

And if bad luck should lay my strength
Into the shallow grave,
Remember all the good you can;
Don't forget my love.

'*Poem*' by John Cornford was copied from *A New Anthology of Modern Verse 1920-1940* edited by C. Day Lewis and L. A. G. Strong.

Sorley MacLean
(Somhairle MacGill-Eain)

Sorley MacLean was born in 1911 on the Isle of Raasay, off Skye. His father was a "tailor-crofter-fisherman". He was educated at Portree High School and at Edinburgh University (where he was a contemporary of Robert Garioch) taking an Honours degree in English ("in order" he said "to let me get a living"). As a student he was writing in both Gaelic and English but felt his English poems derivative, imitative of Pound and Eliot; he concentrated on Gaelic as being truer to himself. He has said, "From the time of my first memories I was very, very, very keen on poetry . . . I was of a family of, I think, unusually good tradition-bearers and singers and pipers on both sides" with the result that "my memory was stored tremendously with Gaelic song". Shelley, particularly political Shelley, was another early enthusiasm. In 1934 he helped MacDiarmid in translating the Gaelic poets Alexander Macdonald and Duncan Macintyre. In the Second World War he served with the Signal Corps in North Africa: "I was wounded twice, very slightly, and then very badly on the last day of the Battle of Alamein. I went up on a landmine." He taught in Portree 1934-37, Tobermory 1938, Edinburgh after the War, and latterly in Plockton, where in 1956 he started teaching Gaelic to non-native speakers. In Plockton he assisted the late Donald Thomson of Oban and other teachers of Gaelic whose work resulted in a great extension of the teaching of Gaelic in secondary schools after 1968: and during his years at Plockton he was one of the earliest pioneers of Comprehensive Education in Scotland. He was Writer in Residence at Edinburgh University 1973-75 and resident Bard at the Gaelic College, Ostaig, Skye 1975-76. Ll.D. Dundee University 1972; D.Litt.Celt. National University of Ireland 1979; D.Litt. Edinburgh University 1980.

Sorley MacLean is the foremost Gaelic poet of this century. His work, in particular *Dàin do Eimhir* (1943), breathed new life into Gaelic poetry, with its mixture of politics (left-wing, Nationalist), literary topics, and autobiographical elements—a very contemporary poetry. A number of poets and critics have testified to the greatness of MacLean's poetry, including George Campbell Hay, Seamus Heaney, Norman MacCaig, Hugh MacDiarmid, Dr John MacInnes, Robert Nye, and Iain Crichton Smith.

Selected Publications

Poetry: *17 poems for 6d: in Gaelic, Lowland Scots and English* (Edinburgh: Chalmers Press 1940. With R. Garioch); *Dàin do Eimhir agus Dàin Eile* (Glasgow: Maclellan 1943); *Lines Review* 34, September 1970 (devoted solely to MacLean's poems); *Poems to Eimhir*, transl. I. C. Smith (Gollancz 1971); *Spring tide and Neap tide: selected poems 1932-1972* (Canongate 1977—parallel Gaelic and English text)

Anthologies: *Honour'd Shade*, ed. N. MacCaig (Chambers 1959); *Contemporary Scottish Verse*, ed. N. MacCaig and A. Scott (Calder 1970); *Four Points of a Saltire* (Gordon Wright 1970—with Stuart MacGregor, William Neill and George Campbell Hay)

Interviews: *Scottish International* 10, May 1970 ("Poetry, Passion and Political Consciousness"); *Studies in Scottish Literature* vol.XIV, 1979; *Radio Times* 20-26th October 1979

Critical Studies: I. C. Smith, "Modern Gaelic Poetry", *Scottish Gaelic Studies* vol. VII, 1953; by Dr. John MacInnes, *Listener* 2nd February 1971 and *Scotsman* 23rd April 1977; Brendan Devlin, "On Sorley MacLean" and John Herdman, "The poetry of Sorley MacLean: a non-Gael's view", both in *Lines Review* 61, June 1977

A selection of MacLean's prose writings is to be published this year by Acair (Stornoway), and most of his poems 1932-1980 by Canongate in Scotland and in America by Iona Press, also this year.

Left: **Sorley MacLean**
Skye, 1980
Photographer: Jessie Ann Matthew

Overleaf: **Edwin Morgan** (1980)
Pencil on cream paper
30¾ × 18¾ inches

Edwin Morgan

Of all poets writing in Britain today, you must be, surely, one of the least provincial. You've translated most of the rated European languages and your work has enormous variety. You're a Glasgow poet and you write Glasgow poems. You write lyrics, concrete poems, science fiction poems. Perhaps some readers wonder at times, "What is constant in all this, what are the common factors here?" It seems to me that one of them is an interest in sheer fact. You have said that you like poetry to come not from poetry itself, but from actuality. How does that attract you? What's the appeal?
I'm not quite sure exactly what the appeal is, except that I've got a kind of feeling that there's a great fund of material for poetry that is not, maybe, sufficiently used . . . I think poets often seem to feel that somehow the media—apart from poetry—have taken over fact. Fact is something for papers or for radio or television, or something of that kind, and less and less, perhaps, is it being used by poets themselves. They, of course, will use it—not necessarily just straight; they'll obviously do something with it. I don't think I'm saying that this is what ought to be at the expense of imagination, because imagination can come into it. Even writing about a factual thing, you have to re-imagine the thing. It goes through a process. So, poetry or art comes in at some stage, but I think there is a great interest in the things that actually do happen. It seems to me, quite often, that things just fly in a great flux all the time. You perhaps read about something or see something and it's gone, and the next day people go on to something else. Yet it might be very interesting just to fix something, go right down close to something, and see what you can make of it.

Could you give us an example of this? An actual moment that has appealed to you?
One of the so-called *Instamatic Poems* might give an example, though in a sense it's not something seen by me,

because these were all poems that were taken from the papers . . . so you're imagining something which actually happened but which you didn't see yourself. **Glasgow 5 March 1971** is perhaps as good an illustration as any. I gave them all the place and the date, just to indicate that this was a factual thing that had actually happened.

With a ragged diamond
of shattered plate-glass
a young man and his girl
are falling backwards into a shop-window.
The young man's face
is bristling with fragments of glass
and the girl's leg has caught
on the broken window
and spurts arterial blood
over her wet-look white coat.
Their arms are starfished out
braced for impact,
their faces show surprise, shock,
and the beginning of pain.
The two youths who have pushed them
are about to complete the operation
reaching into the window
to loot what they can smartly.
Their faces show no expression.
It is a sharp clear night
in Sauchiehall Street.
In the background two drivers
keep their eyes on the road.

It's very violent, very shocking. Are you particularly attracted to violence?
Dangerous question! I think there's something about violence that lends itself to drama, and poetry likes a bit of drama. It's partly that, and it may be partly the place. Not that there are no other violent places than Glasgow, but it often has associations of that kind and clearly there are still many often quite casual violent incidents happening in Glasgow. But no, I don't think it's a positive attraction except in those ways. It is something that you are aware of, particularly in any big city . . . You're aware also—perhaps morally dangerously or wrongly—of the aesthetic possibilities that can be drawn from violence.

I wonder if we could turn now from that poem, in which the identities of the people don't matter— indeed, I suppose the force depends on not knowing who they are—to one of your poems about famous people, where the identity is what the poem takes off from. Like **The Death of Marilyn Monroe.**
It's one of a group of poems that I wrote about people who, as you say, are famous, but who have a kind of legendary quality about them—and she obviously had that.

What innocence? Whose guilt? What eyes? Whose breast?
Crumpled orphan, nembutal bed,
white hearse, Los Angeles,
DiMaggio! Los Angeles! Miller! Los Angeles! America!
That Death should seem the only protector—
That all arms should have faded, and the great cameras and
lights become an inquisition and a torment—
That the many acquaintances, the autograph-hunters, the
inflexible directors, the drive-in admirers should become
a blur of incomprehension and pain—
That lonely Uncertainty should limp up, grinning, with
bewildering barbiturates, and watch her undress and lie
down and in her anguish
call for him! call for him to strengthen her with what could
only dissolve her! A method
of dying, we are shaken, we see it. Strasberg!
Los Angeles! Olivier! Los Angeles! Others die
and yet by this death we are a little shaken, we feel it,
America.
Let no one say communication is a cantword.
They had to lift her hand from the bedside telephone.
But what she had not been able to say
perhaps she had said. 'All I had was my life.
I have no regrets, because if I made
any mistakes, I was responsible.
There is now—and there is the future.
What has happened is behind. So

it follows you around? So what?'—This
to a friend, ten days before.
And so she was responsible.
And if she was not responsible, not wholly responsible, Los Angeles? Los Angeles? Will it follow you around? Will the slow white hearse of the child of America follow you around?

There's still this fascination with fact, isn't there?
There is, yes. The detail that is there and was somehow felt to be important. I suppose it's partly again like the last poem—something that comes not directly from experience, but from reading about something from newspapers: reports of her suicide and accounts of people who had known her very well, and so on. Many of the details come from actual newspaper accounts . . . so it is not unlike the other poem . . . though it lets itself go in a new sort of way . . . The kind of underlying hysteria, I suppose, of the whole Hollywood background of the star system . . . to bring out a sense of her victimization . . .

This interest in fact goes back a long time in your history, doesn't it? I've read your reminiscence about your father telling you how steel was made, and your being interested in the scientific data on cigarette cards.
Yes. Under the bedclothes!

That leads eventually into your interest in science fiction and writing poems which might reasonably be called science fiction poems. Could you say something about how you arrived at this interest?
I think it comes partly, as you say, from this interest in facts and in the idea that things scientific can be interesting because of what they are, even apart from any appeal to imagination. But I think the imagination begins to come in very quickly, because I remember these old sets of cigarette cards were usually called something like 'Wonders of Nature.' The element of wonder was always there—partly as a selling device, perhaps, to sugar the pill. I did feel, at a very early age, the wonder of these things . . . It's like the steel-making process. Before I had seen anything visual about it in a film, or anything of that kind, it was just my father telling me about it. He must have told it very vividly, because I could actually imagine that I could see this kind of thing. It was both very factual . . . he had to know the whole process, all its details . . . but at the same time the imaginative appeal was very strong. So perhaps from that it seemed to me to be useful to go into science fiction because it could bring these two things together: it could be based on scientific or technological fact, and it could also stimulate the imagination very strongly.

I think the most powerful of your science fiction poems are those which go beyond the wonder of scientific data and achievement and proceed to say something more basic about the human condition . . . One of the most interesting examples of this is the poem entitled 'In Sobieski's Shield.' *Sobieski's Shield* is the name of one of the distant constellations and, very briefly, the poem is about people being saved from some catastrophe that's hit the world, by being beamed to this very distant world and re-materialized at the other end . . .

Your tone in the poem is tense. I'm frightened. The change is violent; sensations are stringent. The father's lost a finger, the son's lost a nipple, the wife's hair is beautiful but she's frightened too. British Rail sounds easier. How frightened should I be? How austere is this very complex poem of speculation and prediction meant to be?
. . . It's got its frightening element, but I wouldn't think this was the thing that's meant to come from it in the end. The idea is that this has been done for the first time. It's not the easy beaming-up you get in 'Star Trek'! . . . Nobody knows what's going to happen, and therefore they go through this really awfully traumatic experience. But they get through it, they do wake up. They're slightly changed and they have this problem of trying to decide if they are the same people . . . The conclusion they're coming to is that they are, in fact, although these things have happened to them. They can . . . take up the threads in this distant world, and go out and try to make some sense of it, try to survive. In fact, it's about survival, I suppose, as much as about

anything else. But it's partly that, and partly the feeling that whatever difficulties they've got, it's just a kind of carrying forward from other difficulties that people have got through before, and the references to the First World War are presumably important in that sense. There's this chain of lives, of people going through terrible things but coming through and surviving.

Let's have a love poem.

From a City Balcony:

How often when I think of you the day grows bright!
Our silent love
wanders in Glen Fruin with butterflies and cuckoos—
bring me the drowsy country thing! Let it drift above
 the traffic
by the open window with a cloud of witnesses—
a sparkling burn, white lambs, the blaze of gorse,
the cuckoos calling madly, the real white clouds over us,
white butterflies about your hand in the short hot grass,
and then the witness was my hand closing on yours,
my mouth brushing your eyelids and your lips
again and again till you sighed and turned for love.
Your breast and thighs were blazing like the gorse.
I covered your great fire in silence there.
We let the day grow old along the grass.
It was in the silence the love was.

Footsteps and witnesses! In this Glasgow balcony who pours
such joy like mountain water? It brims, it spills over and over
down to the parched earth and the relentless wheels.
How often will I think of you, until
our dying steps forget this light, forget
that we ever knew the happy glen,
or that I ever said, We must jump into the sun,
and we jumped into the sun.

That poem is irrefutably romantic in very straightforward, obvious ways. Could this be an answer to the kind of criticism that has been levelled at your work, that you do stay hidden, that you are warm—but a little icy too . . .?
I don't think this is really true . . . I'm quite sure I'm in the poems far more than is sometimes said . . . Often, of course, it's at a remove. You can write about yourself directly; you can appear to write about yourself directly and not be doing it . . . but I would think that a lot of the poems I write do project either me or a part of me into some other circumstance, and eventually it would be seen that these are all aspects of me . . . So I would project myself into other existences, perhaps other people, like the apple, or even like the hyena or the Loch Ness Monster, or whatever. I enter . . . into these creatures, and presumably, if the poems work at all, if I get any joy out of doing it, there must be something in me that goes out to things like that, and, therefore, I am talking about things that appeal to me . . .

This ability to spread your responses, spread your joy in the world across such a wide range, seems to me to indicate a fundamentally romantic disposition. Would you accept that you are, after all the concrete poems and the meticulous and remarkable games with words, fundamentally a romantic poet?
I think probably this is true. I think it has all sorts of qualifications, in the sense that I am very interested in structure and form as well as in feeling. Fundamentally . . . it was always romantic poetry that appealed to me strongly when I began to write, and I still find I very often come back to it. I don't, on the whole, like eighteenth-century poetry. So there's something to this . . . but there are also various kinds of control and structure that appeal to me very strongly.

Control and structure are both evident in your long sequence of poems, The New Divan. *Meanings are not always as obvious. It's a long poem which, I think, can make a very immediate appeal in terms of its images and language. It's a very provocative poem. It commands in these kinds of ways, but I think many readers may be puzzled by it . . . I wonder if I could ask you to look at the opening lines of poem 81.*

The night is over, the lark is singing,
the sages sit in full divan
in the anteroom of heaven,
the water bubbles, the pipe is sweet.
A pigeon calls over the marshes,
flaps across the anteroom glass.
Every room's a window where
sages turn the innocent pages
and turn the earth slowly around.

That's a marvellous image of the sages turning the pages—but what are they seeing? It seems to suggest that here we have a metaphor for the poem itself: the poems are windows through which the sages look, through which we try to look. The world, in this long poem, is revolved—and we can see its facets if we look carefully. Can you help us to see; can you give us a hint about how we should look?
I don't know how much I can give in the way of hints about that, because, as you say, the whole world is swivelling around, and, in a sense, it's all there. But I suppose the setting of the poem is meant to be a kind of key in that it's the Middle East and it's about the past—the ancient past as well as the more recent past. It's about war. It's about ancient history and archaeology, and it's a mixture of things that have happened, especially during the last war, when I was in the Middle East, and things that I, perhaps, imagine happening and dramatise. So it's very hard to say that it's doing one thing. It's dramatising certain ideas about history and man's place in history and the idea of the sages sitting in divan, casting their eyes over everything, is probably fairly central, though it's also just one little instant in the poem. Although I mentioned the word 'structure' earlier, I don't regard this poem as being necessarily highly structured. I'd like poeple to be able to read it in a much more easy and flexible way than that.

How much of a Scottish or a Glasgow poet do you think you are?
Well, I certainly feel to be a Scottish poet and also a Glasgow poet in the sense that I've always lived in Glasgow and do recurrently write about it. I think you get labels that only work up to a point. One can accept being called a Glasgow poet as long as the other things are regarded as being part of the whole picture. I like to have a base. Although I travel about quite a bit, I like to have Glasgow to return to, and naturally I will write about it many times, but the other things are very important . . . The desire to use the imagination is probably just as strong as the thing we started off talking about, the use of fact. Both things are probably equally important, and in *The New Divan* the idea was to bring the two together . . . It is very down to earth and realistic in some ways; in other ways it is a fantasy . . . But it's probably a kind of pendulum thing. The local thing will tend to be the realistic side of it; other things will tend to introduce imagination—and there's a good deal of swinging back and forth between the two.

Edwin Morgan (1980). Pastel on paper, 26 × 19¼ inches (detail)

You do write about your city with great delight as well as with a perception of its possible horrors.

Yes, I do. I like, if possible, to show the different sides of it. It's easy to get the melodrama of a big city, including its violence; but if other things are happening that are happier, hopeful, it's good to bring them into poetry, as I try to do in some poems like **Trio:**

Coming up Buchanan Street, quickly, on a sharp winter evening
a young man and two girls, under the Christmas lights—
The young man carries a new guitar in his arms,
the girl on the inside carries a very young baby,
and the girl on the outside carries a chihuahua.
And the three of them are laughing, their breath rises
in a cloud of happiness, and as they pass
the boy says, 'Wait till he sees this but!'
The chihuahua has a tiny Royal Stewart tartan coat like a teapot-
  holder,
the baby in its white shawl is all bright eyes and mouth like favours
  in a fresh sweet cake,
the guitar swells out under its milky plastic cover, tied at the neck
  with silver tinsel tape and a brisk sprig of mistletoe.
Orphean sprig! Melting baby! Warm chihuahua!
The vale of tears is powerless before you.
Whether Christ is born, or is not born, you
put paid to fate, it abdicates
                under the Christmas lights.
Monsters of the year
go blank, are scattered back,
can't bear this march of three.

And the three have passed, vanished in the crowd—
(yet not vanished, for in their arms they wind
the life of men and beasts, and music,
laughter ringing them round like a guard)
at the end of this winter's day.

Glasgow 20th September 1980

Eve and Adam

Adam sleeps so sound
I sometimes raise myself on one elbow
and look at him I cannot say how long
in the darkness. Nightingale,
owl, cricket—everything is music.
A trace of moonlight falls on his face.
I bend, and brush it with my breasts, but he
sleeps on, and never, never will he know.
I have another secret: I call to the owl,
not loud, and he as gently answers me.
How friendly all the creatures are! I love them
but neither language nor music can tell
what I feel for Adam—even his black hair
lying tangled in a helpless mass
over his shoulders, nothing, nothing
to his eyes, his voice, his hands, holds me
as the web of trees, unknowing,
holds the night-clouds and the moon. Oh
but if I am the moon I move, I pass into shadow,
I roll far from him and from myself, I lie back
staring into deepest darkness, lift my arm
for the great moth to light on purring in white fur
and whisper to him
in a waft of tansy,
'I have forgotten Adam.'
—Tonight I cannot sleep, cannot wake, cannot dream,
                                        seem
suspended like a woody pool reflecting woods
and sky and clouds, unreal and more than real
their world, unreal and more than real
my soul, diffused in wonder and surmise
above a body I have lost,
glimmering spreadeagled in eglantine.
—The moth crawls down my flank like Adam's finger,
the moon floods through our careless arbour roof,
I am so much awake I can hear the waterfalls
that feed our lively, seldom-mirroring pools,
and Adam's heart against my breast.
I hear it all and feel it all, and almost cry

my longing as he twitches in his dream
and clasp him, saying at his ear
what I have seen where I have been,
my secrets, to his silence,
and twine my hand in his until he wakens
shouting; comfort him; love him;
blot him from the distant stars.
Soon it will be grey. He has forgotten his dream.
I am the one who remembers dreams.
The blackbird sings. I shall make a comb for my hair.

Jack London in Heaven

Part the clouds, let me look down.
Oh god that earth. A breeze comes from the sea
and humpback fogs blanch off to blindness, the sun
hits Frisco, it shines solid up to heaven.
I can't bear not to see a brisk day on the Bay,
it drives me out of my mind but I can't bear
not to watch the choppy waters, Israfel.
I got a sea-eagle once to come up here
screaming and turn a prayer-wheel or two
with angry buffets till the sharpshooters
sent him to hell, and I groaned,
grew dark with disfavour. —What,
I should pray now? For these thoughts?
Here are some more. I was up at four
for psalms, shawms, smarms, salaams, yessirs, yesmaams,
felt-tipped hosannas melting into mist,
a mushroom high, an elation of vapours,
a downpour of dumpy amens. Azazel,
I am sick of fireflies. It's a dumb joss.
—You know I'm a spoilt angel? What happens to us?
I'm not so bright—or bright, perhaps. God knows!
They almost let me fall through heaven craning
to see sunshine dappling the heaving gunmetal
of the Oakland Estuary—the crawl, the swell, the crests
I could pull up to touch and wet my hands
let down a moment into time and space.
How long will they allow me to remember
as I pick the cloud-rack apart and peer?
The estuary, Israfel, the glittery estuary, August '96!
My last examination has scratched to a finish,
I'm rushing to the door, whooping and squawking,
I dance down the steps, throw my hat in the air
as the dusty invigilator frowns, gathers in
that furious harvest of four months' cramming,
nineteen hours a day—my vigils, Azazel,
my holy vigils—the oyster-pirate hammering
at the gates of the state university.
It's enough. I got in. But at that time
I took a boat out on the ebb
to be alone where no book ever was.
I scudded dreaming through the creamy rings
of light and water, followed the shore
and thought of earth and heaven and myself
till I saw a shipyard I knew, and the delta rushes
and the weeds and the tin wharves, and smelt the ropes
and some tobacco-smoke, and longed for company.
—Evensong? I'm not coming to evensong.
Get off, get away. Go on, sing for your supper!
Bloody angels! —So I sailed in, made fast,
and there was Charley, and Liz, and Billy and Joe, and Dutch
—that desperate handsome godlike drunken man—
old friends, Azazel, old friends that clambered over me
and sang and wept and filled me with whisky and beer
brought teetering across the railroad tracks
all that long noon.
They would have kept me there, oh, for ever
but I could see the blue through the open door,
that blue, my sea, and they knew
I had to be away, and got me stumbling down the wharf steps
into a good salmon boat, with charcoal and a brazier
and coffee and a pot and a pan and a fresh-caught fish
and cast me off into a stiff wind.
I tell you, Israfel, the sea was white
and half of it was in my boat
with my sail set hard like a board.
Everything whipped and cracked
in pure green glory as
I stood braced at the mast
and roared out 'Shenandoah'.
Did Odysseus get to heaven?

I came down to earth, at Antioch,
sobered in the sunset shadows, tied up
alongside a potato sloop, had friends
aboard there too, who sizzled my fish for me
and gave me stew and crusty bread and claret,
claret in great pint mugs, and wrapped me in blankets
warmer and softer than the clouds of heaven.
What did we not talk of as we smoked,
sea-tales Odysseus might have known,
under the same night wind, the same wild rigging.
—Azazel, I must get down there!
I am a wasting shade, I am drifting and dying
by these creeping streams. If you are my friend,
tell them my trouble. Tell them
they cannot make me a heaven
like the tide-race and the tiller
and a broken-nailed hand
and the shrouds of Frisco.

'In a Convex Mirror,' Etc.

Painting Ashbery under water
is like reading a trimaran in wavering light
in August, or later if the plums are home
dry, and the must is setting in wistfully
or as the last letter came out with, 'after all,'
and that is hardly a blanket
to wrap braves in. They come and go,
swilling the waves and dying of it,
rising like red fruit to break the Vinland clods,
marrying and mastering these misguided summers.
What are paints for but giving change?
To be bound, tightly, and made to lie and fret
in a floating cradle is a caterpillar
of another colour than catalogued, and oil
slides off the propeller as if paralyzed.
Terminally, all the posts go dark.
Put earth in the basket for a rainy day.
It comes at the very end, as the watchers disperse
they hear the swirl of a giant moray
nosing the burnt umber of the background, still wet.

The Coals

Before my mother's hysterectomy
she cried, and told me she must never bring
coals in from the cellar outside the house,
someone must do it for her. The thing itself
I knew was nothing, it was the thought
of that dependence. Her tears shocked me
like a blow. As once she had been taught,
I was taught self-reliance, discipline,
which is both good and bad. You get things done,
you feel you keep the waste and darkness back
by acts and acts and acts and acts and acts,
bridling if someone tells you this is vain,
learning at last in pain. Hardest of all
is to forgive yourself for things undone,
guilt that can poison life—away with it,
you say, and it is loath to go away.
I learned both love and joy in a hard school
and treasure them like the fierce salvage of
some wreck that has been built to look like stone
and stand, though it did not, a thousand years.

Left: **Edwin Morgan**
Glasgow, 1980
Photographer: Jessie Ann Matthew

Page 85: **Edwin Morgan** 1980
Oil on canvas, 60¼ × 39¾ inches

Edwin George Morgan

Edwin Morgan was born on 27th April 1920 in Glasgow, where his father was a clerk with a firm of scrap merchants, later a director. He was educated at Rutherglen Academy, Glasgow High School, and Glasgow University. He took his degree, in English, after war service with the Royal Army Medical Corps (also MacDiarmid's regiment), mainly in the Middle East, 1940-46. He lectured in English at Glasgow University from 1947 until last year (1980), when he retired: as Assistant Lecturer 1947-50, Lecturer 1950-65, Senior Lecturer 1965-71, Reader 1971-75, and from 1975 as Titular Professor.
Awards: Cholmondeley Award 1968; SAC awards 1968, 1973, 1975, 1977, 1978; Hungarian P.E.N. Memorial Medal 1972.

As well as poet Morgan is a translator of some eminence (into Scots and English of Anglo-Saxon, Russian, Italian, French, and German poetry), editor, anthologist, critic, librettist, and an internationally known practitioner of concrete/visual poetry and 'sound poems'. His recreations have been listed as including colour photography, scrapbooks, and looking at cities.

He began writing at school, concentrating more on prose than poetry, "creating huge fantastic narratives", reflecting his early interest in science fiction—an interest he has never lost but which is now manifested in verse, in his 'science fiction poems'. His early verse was romantic, and modern verse and foreign language poetry did not make an impact until university; further influences were the Beats and Black Mountain poets in the 1950s and the Brazilian concrete poets in the early '60s.

Morgan is possibly best known in Scotland for his Glasgow poems—of people and place—poems of "passionate observation": poetry in his view should "acknowledge its environment": "I like a poetry that comes not out of 'poetry' but out of a story in today's newspaper, or a chance personal encounter in a city street, or the death of a famous person: I am very strongly moved by the absolute force of what actually happens . . ." Poetry he thinks of "as partly an instrument of exploration, like a spaceship, into new fields of feeling, or experience . . . and partly a special way of recording moments and events (taking the 'prose' of them, the grit of the facts of the case, as being in our age extremely important)." (Edwin Morgan in *Worlds*, p.229)

Selected Publications

Poetry: *The Vision of Cathkin Braes* (Maclellan 1952); *Starryveldt* (Eugen Gomringer 1965); *The Second Life* (EUP 1968); *Instamatic Poems* (Ian McKelvie 1972); *From Glasgow to Saturn* (Carcanet 1973); *The New Divan* (Carcanet 1977); *Star gate: science fiction poems* (Third Eye Centre 1979)
Anthologies: *Penguin Modern Poets 15* (1969); *A Sense of Belonging* (Blackie 1977)

Translations: *Beowulf* (California University Press 1962, Hand & Flower Press 1952, Officina Pluralo 1980); *Sovpoems* (Migrant Press 1961); *Wi the Haill Voice: 25 poems by Vladimir Mayakovsky* (Carcanet 1972); *Rites of Passage: (selected) translations* (Carcanet 1976)

Prose: *Essays* (Carcanet 1974); *Hugh MacDiarmid* (Writers & their Work series, 1976)

Edited: *Scottish Satirical Verse: an anthology* (Carcanet 1980)

Critical studies: R. Fulton, *Contemporary Scottish Poetry,* 1974, pp. 13-40; M. Schmidt, *Fifty British Poets,* Pan Books 1979, pp. 314-20

Interview: M. Walker, *Edwin Morgan: an interview,* Akros, 1977

See also: E. Morgan, "Notes on One Poet's Working Day" in Poetry Dimension 2, ed. D. Abse, 1974
Worlds: seven modern poets, ed. G. Summerfield (Penguin 1974), pp. 226-61
Edwin Morgan: a selected bibliography 1950-1980, compiled by Hamish Whyte (Mitchell Library, 1980)

CONTRIBUTORS: Biographical Details

Alexander Moffat was born in Dunfermline in 1943. He was a student at Edinburgh College of Art from 1960-64: a love of Léger's paintings and a commitment to socialism led him to work in an engineering factory and as a photographer until 1968. In 1969 he became Chairman of the New 57 Gallery in Edinburgh, a position he held until 1978.

In 1973 he had an important one-man exhibition at the Scottish National Portrait Gallery, *A View of the Portrait*—Portraits by Alexander Moffat, 1968-1973. (Included in this exhibition were several literary portraits—the poets Alan Bold, Alan Jackson, and Norman MacCaig and the novelist Archie Hind). In 1975 he had an exhibition at the Gallery of the Warsaw Press Club in Warsaw; he has taken part in important group exhibitions: at the Fruit Market Gallery in Edinburgh 1975 (with Bellany, Dallas Brown, Gillon); the *Human Clay* exhibition in 1976, the *Narrative Paintings: Figurative Art of Two Generations* exhibition in 1979, and was also responsible for selecting an exhibition of Peter de Francia's work at the Camden Arts Centre in 1977.

His series of paintings *Berliners* which featured the Scottish journalist Neal Ascherson and his friends Rudi Dutschke and Ulrike Meinhof was shown at the Midland Group Gallery, Nottingham in 1978.

Alexander Moffat has works in many major British Collections and has been teaching at Glasgow School of Art since 1979.

Timothy Hyman was born in 1946 and educated at Charterhouse and The Slade School of Art, London. He is a painter and organised and exhibited with Alexander Moffat in *Narrative Paintings* (Arnolfini, Bristol; I.C.A., London; The Fruit Market Gallery, Edinburgh 1979-80). Mixed exhibitions include Blond Fine Art 1980; a one-man show is scheduled for 1981. He writes regularly on art for *The London Magazine* and is a contributing editor to *Artscribe.* (Longer articles include: Beckmann, Léger, Kitaj, Hodgkin, De Francia, Balthus). He has lectured for London and Sussex Universities, and for many British art schools.

Neal Ascherson was born in Edinburgh in 1932. He has spent most of his life as a foreign correspondant, but from 1975 to 1979 worked on *The Scotsman* as a writer on Scottish politics. He is a regular literary critic for the *New York Review of Books* and *The Observer.* He works as a foreign reporter on *The Observer* for half the year and is currently working on a book for Penguin on Polish strikes and the new Trade Union movement which emerged in the summer of 1980.

He is the author of *The King Incorporated; Leopold II in the Age of Trusts* (1963), and editor of *The Times and the French Revolution* (1975). He has compiled a "political diary" of Scottish politics in the year 1977 for the North Sea Oil Panel of The Social Sciences Research Council, but for legal reasons this is not being published at the moment.

Marshall Walker was born in Glasgow and educated at Jordanhill College School, Glasgow University and Jordanhill College of Education. After a year of teaching in Glasgow schools he went to South Africa where he lectured in English at Rhodes University. In 1965 he joined the English Department of Glasgow University where he has been especially associated with the teaching of American literature. He has held several visiting professorships in the U.S.A. and has recently been appointed Professor of English and Head of Department at the University of Waikato in Hamilton, New Zealand. Marshall Walker is author of critical articles, short fiction and *Robert Penn Warren: A Vision Earned* (1979). *Edwin Morgan: An Interview* was published by Akros in 1977. He is at present writing a history of American literature.

Hamish Whyte was born in Renfrewshire in 1947 and educated in Glasgow. Since 1978 he has been Senior Librarian, Rare Books and Manuscripts Department, Mitchell Library, Glasgow.

His publications include: *apple on an orange day: poems* (Autolycus 1973); edited *Lady Castlehill's Receipt Book* (Molendinar 1976); *Arran Poems* (forthcoming, Arran Gallery Press 1981); *Rooms* (forthcoming, Aquila Press 1981); *Anthology of Glasgow Poems 1930-80* (forthcoming, Third Eye Centre 1981).

Poems, reviews in: *Akros, Asphalt Garden, Library Review, Scottish Review, Words, etc.*

Jessie Ann Matthew was educated at Oxenford Castle School, East Lothian, and at the Central School of Art and Design, London. From 1976-1980 she has been carrying out freelance photography work in Scotland and London. She is currently working with a group of women photographers taking pictures of women for an exhibition sponsored by the Half Moon Gallery, London to tour the U.K. in 1981.

Previous exhibitions include: *Women* (now touring), *Men* (now touring), both Half Moon Gallery exhibitions; and *Ballet Rambert Workshop,* shown at Riverside Studios, London.

Her photographs have appeared in a number of publications including *The London Magazine, The Observer* Colour Magazine, *The London Magazine, The Observer* Colour Magazine, *The Radio Times,* and *The British Journal of Photography Year Book.*